FLORENCE SCHECHTER

Illustrated by Nadia Akingbule

PENGUIN BOOKS

PENGUIN BOOKS

UK | USA | Canada | Ireland | Australia
India | New Zealand | South Africa

Penguin Books is part of the Penguin Random House group of companies
whose addresses can be found at global.penguinrandomhouse.com.

www.penguin.co.uk   www.puffin.co.uk   www.ladybird.co.uk

First published 2023

001

Printed in Dubai

The authorized representative in the EEA is Penguin Random House Ireland,
Morrison Chambers, 32 Nassau Street, Dublin D02 YH68

A CIP catalogue record for this book is available from the British Library

ISBN: 978–0–241–56144–7

All correspondence to:
Penguin Books
One Embassy Gardens, 8 Viaduct Gardens, London SW11 7BW

For Miriam – the only person
born from the same vagina I was.

Contents

/viː/

noun

A gender-inclusive term for the vulva, vagina and gynaecological anatomy. It is a symbol of power, pleasure and celebration. It describes the part of the body that includes:

- the vulva (the external genitalia, which includes the mons pubis, labia, clitoris, vaginal and urethral openings);

- the internal gynaecological organs (including the vagina, cervix, uterus, ovarian tubes and ovaries).

A Clitroduction

I love my vulva.

It's my favourite part of my body. It's closely followed by my brain (because it does weird things that make me laugh), my smile (which is a cliché but true) and my boobs (because they're bangin' and I make no apology for it).

I love how my vulva looks – my right inner labium is twice the width of my left one, which I think is pretty interesting. I love how it brings me pleasure – shout out to my clitoris. I love my pubic hair too – does anyone else twiddle theirs when they're feeling fidgety, or is that just me? I love how learning about my vulva has allowed me to realize its power, fight against stigma, grow in confidence, prioritize my pleasure and find my 'Big V Energy'.

I LOVE my vulva. And by the end of this book, I hope you'll love yours too.

Back in 2017, I was moaning to my friend Melissa about the lack of research into animal vaginas. I'd recently made a video about my top-ten most fascinating animal penises[1] and I was attempting to create a vagina sequel. But I was struggling to find more than a few interesting examples. Melissa told me that she had recently visited a penis museum in Iceland, so perhaps there was a vagina museum I could visit to find out more? But alas, none existed.

I found an Austrian-based website (www.vaginamuseum.at) and the Royal College of Obstetricians and Gynaecologists by-appointment-only medical museum. Around the world, there were some related museums, including sex museums and women's museums, the Museum of Contraception and Abortion in Vienna and the Museum of Motherhood in Florida. But there was no place I could visit where I could ask a gallery assistant why duck vaginas are labyrinthine and shaped like a corkscrew.[2] So I decided to open my own vagina museum.

And I did what any overly online person does and immediately tweeted about it, on 20 March 2017. By 2019, we had our first premises in London's Camden Market, then, in 2022, we got an even bigger building in Bethnal Green. And with each passing year, my love of the V grows.

This book is all about starting your journey towards loving your V – and I truly believe that love comes from understanding. How can we take care of our bodies if we don't know how they work? How can we celebrate our bodies if we don't use the right words? And how can we become activists if we don't know what we're fighting for? We're going to learn all about the gynaecological anatomy; how to confidently talk about your body; be honest about sex; learn about the changes and

---

1 Barnacles were number one, if you were wondering. You can google it to find out why.

2 Don't worry, I found out – it's so that female ducks can lead unwanted penises down the wrong path to prevent conception.

cycles your body goes through, such as periods and menopause; the religions that once worshipped the vulva and the art that glorifies it; how you can become a vagina-loving activist; and

SO.
MUCH.
MORE.

But as much as this book is going to be about celebrating the V, there are going to be some tough topics we'll need to cover too. There will be specific trigger warnings at the start of some of the chapters, but as a general note, we'll be talking about sex, health, contraception, abortion, sexism, racism, consent and some generally pretty tough topics. It would be impossible to write a book about Vs that is 100 per cent positive – and to do so would be to ignore some pretty vital things from history through to the present day. We cannot empower ourselves without acknowledging why that empowerment is needed.

Throughout, you'll also read Vagina Dialogues – short pieces from lots of exciting people. This book covers loads of topics, and it's always best to learn directly from people who have relevant experiences. Bear in mind, though, that no community is a monolith, which means that each and every community in our vast, diverse world contains people with a huge range of backgrounds, political views, experiences and perspectives. So just because one person within a community believes something, it doesn't mean everyone does. I have also included some fun stories from loads of really great people because this is a celebration of the V, after all!

There's so much more that could have been included in this book, and if I went in depth for every single related topic, this book would have ended up being longer than *Encyclopaedia*

Britannica.[3] So remember, each page is just the surface of an ocean. If there's a topic you want to learn more about, check out the resources at the end of the book. You'll also find a glossary at the back too.

There's one caveat I'd like to make before we get going. I'm writing this in the UK, where we have the NHS – which is almost definitely the best thing Britain has ever created. Because of this, I say 'go and see your doctor if you want to know more' quite a lot. I recognize that if you live in a country where you have to pay for healthcare, this might not always be possible as it could get very expensive very quickly.[4] If there's something worrying you about your body, try to speak to a professional if you can, as they will be the best source of information. However, I hope this book will ease some of your concerns about your wonderful body and identify what you might not need to ask a doctor about, as it may be that what you're worrying about is actually totally normal.

Our bodies are wonderful, complicated things. They don't always work in the way we think they will, and they often surprise us and leave us in awe. This is especially true for our V. The V brings us pleasure and pain. Sometimes it bleeds. Sometimes it makes new humans. And sometimes it doesn't. The V is powerful and deserves all the recognition and celebration this world can give it.

3   Coming soon to all bookstores: *Encyclopaedia Vulvanica.*

4   That's why I genuinely believe that free healthcare is a basic human right and a feminist issue – but that's a discussion for another book.

And so, with definitions, caveats and personal history aside, let us start the journey together towards loving your V

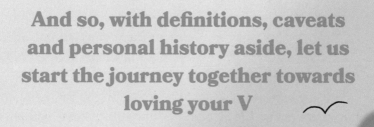

This book is intended to be enjoyed by people aged 14+. So if you're around this age, firstly, welcome – you are clearly cool and happening.

If you're in the slightly older camp, also welcome! I hope this book will be useful and enjoyed by everyone who is ready to embark on this journey, whether you're 14, 44 or 104. Just replace any references to school and other young-people things with 'workplace' or whatever is relevant to your life.

Important words every vulva-lover should know

Before we get going, here's a short rundown of some words I'll be using throughout. (There's also a longer glossary at the back, on page 286.) Words referring to anatomy will be well covered in more detail in the first chapter, and words related to sexuality and gender will be covered in chapters 4 and 8.

It's important to remember that language changes over time and something that might have once been appropriate might be inappropriate now or in the future. Equally, some words that were previously thought of as offensive can have their meaning changed or reclaimed.

Feminism: There are so many definitions of feminism, but my favourite is the one by feminist scholar bell hooks: 'Feminism is a movement to end sexism, sexist exploitation and oppression.'

Sex: In short, sex is understood as a person's biological characteristics, including their chromosomes, genitals and hormones (but we'll soon learn that it's more complicated than this!).

Gender: While sex is biological, gender is cultural and includes traits such as behaviours, expressions and identity (again, very complicated, as we will soon learn!).

Cisgender: An adjective that describes someone whose gender matches the one they were assigned at birth.

Transgender: An adjective that describes someone whose gender doesn't match the one they were assigned at birth.

Non-binary: The idea that there are only two genders (male and female) can be called a 'gender binary'. Non-binary is an umbrella term for when a person's gender doesn't fall into either of these two genders.

Marginalized genders: An umbrella term for people who have been oppressed due to their gender. It includes women, trans people, non-binary people and many more.

Patriarchy: A social system where cis men hold power over women and people of marginalized genders.

Kyriarchy: A term coined by feminist theologian Professor Elisabeth Schüssler Fiorenza in 1992. It refers to how our society is made up of multiple systems of oppression that interact with each other to dominate marginalized groups. These systems include the patriarchy, white supremacy, homophobia, transphobia, capitalism, colonialism and more.

Intersectionality: Though a very old concept, the word itself was coined by civil rights scholar Professor Kimberlé Crenshaw in 1989. It refers to how different systems of oppression interconnect to create specific, overlapping types of discrimination. For example, Dr Moya Bailey, a professor of gender studies and Africana studies, coined the term 'misogynoir', which refers to a specific form of oppression experienced by Black women that combines sexism and racism.

A QUICK NOTE ON SEX AND GENDER

Not everyone with a vagina is a woman, and not every woman has a vagina. The same goes for penises and men. Non-binary people can have any genitalia. I'll be using gendered terms here carefully. For example, when discussing things that don't really have anything to do with gender and are purely biological, I'll be using phrases such as 'people with vulvas' and 'people with penises'. When we're talking about societal stuff, I will often (but not always) use 'women' and 'men' because it is society that has traditionally stated that woman = vagina and man = penis.

Chapter 1
ANATOMY 101

Before opening the Vagina Museum, I decided it would be a good idea to brush up on gynaecology. I searched online for common textbooks used in medical schools and came across one that seemed well reviewed but also, most importantly, had been uploaded online for free.[5] I learnt in alarming detail about how the uterus is made of layers, discovered long words such as *fossa navicularis* and all sorts of other complicated stuff. Then I came across something that made me think twice about not only the book but about how the whole of science and medicine is taught. Under the section titled 'Vaginal orifice and hymen', it read: '*The hymen is usually ruptured at the consummation of marriage.*' Not only does the hymen not 'rupture' (as we'll learn about soon), it's also quite possible to have sex before marriage. Surely doctors know this?! After all, that book was published in 2013!!!

With so much misinformation out there, I want to set the record straight with important facts, such as:

- **Hymens don't break.**
- **Long inner labia are normal.**
- **Vulvas aren't shameful.**

And much, much more.

This book is all about celebrating your V, and knowledge is power. The first step to loving your body is to know it. It's time to learn what a vulva actually is.

---

5   You don't work in museums to make money.

VULVA

The external part of the genitalia

Mons pubis
The fatty bit located north of the clitoris on top of the pubic bone.

Glans clitoris
Usually just referred to as the clitoris, it is the only organ in the human body that's sole function is sexual pleasure. On some people you can see it clearly and on others it's covered by the clitoral hood.

Urethral opening
Where the wee comes out of. (Yep, different hole!)

Vaginal opening
The vagina doesn't stay open like a gaping hole for things to wander in and out. The walls are pressed together and only expand if something is going in or out.

Fourchette
The place where the inner labia meet at the base of the vulva.

Anus
Cards on the table, the anus isn't part of the vulva. But it's just so . . . there! The anus is where poo comes out of.

Sometimes there are tiny little bumps on the skin of the vulva called Fordyce spots. They are light in colour, totally painless and about 1–3 mm in width. They are sebaceous glands, which means they make sweat and grow hair. They also occur around the mouth and on penises, and are completely normal.

Pubic hair
Pubic hair, which starts to grow during puberty, protects the vulva from friction and traps moisture to keep the skin soft and healthy. The follicles that grow pubic hair have sweat glands that produce odour.

Vestibule
The area between the two inner lips where the urethral and vaginal openings sit.

Labia minora
Thin flaps without hair on. Also called 'inner labia' or 'inner lips'. They swell with blood when you're aroused. They also protect the vestibule.

Lesser vestibular glands
Little glands in the vestibule near the urethra. Also called the Skene's glands.

Labia majora
The fatty flaps also called 'outer labia' or 'outer lips'. The outer-facing parts are dry and have hair on. The inner facing sides are hairless and moist.

Greater vestibular glands
Small glands in the vestibule near the vaginal opening that make the wetness when you're aroused. Also called the Bartholin's glands.

Perineum
The area of skin between the base of the labia and the anus.

NO TWO VULVAS LOOK THE SAME

Have you ever looked at your vulva and thought, *does this look normal?* I've got something **big** to tell you: there's no such thing as normal. Every person's body is different – and that's just as true for vulvas.

Labia minora are probably the most diverse part. They can range from 7–50 mm in width, and it's not uncommon for them to be even wider than this. They range from 20–100 mm in length. Sometimes they are big enough to stick out from the labia majora – this is **totally** normal. Often, they are asymmetrical. Mine are!

Labia also massively vary in colour and can either be the same colour as the rest of your skin or be redder, pinker, browner or even a shade of purple! It's super common for labia to change with age – particularly when you go through puberty and menopause – and when you're aroused. They don't change with how much sex you have though! That's a total myth – it's literally impossible to establish someone's sexual history from the appearance of their vulva.

The illustrations on this page are drawn from real people's vulvas. Look how diverse they are!

Take some time to grab a mirror and gaze at your vulva to see how unique and beautiful it really is.

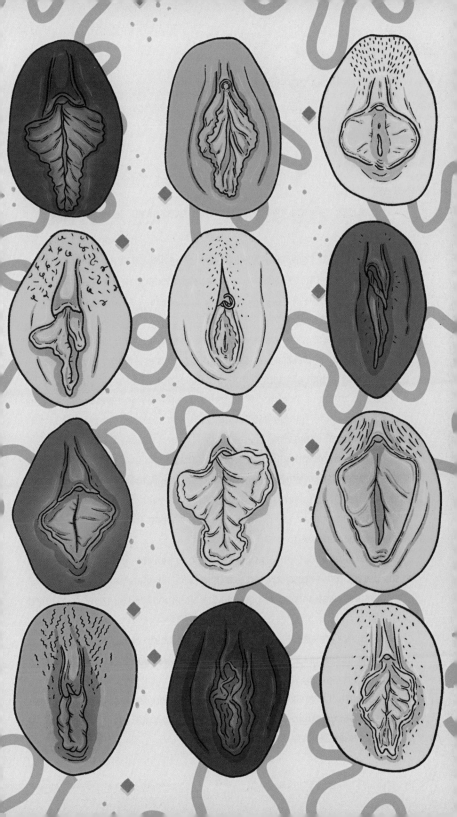

Dr Ronx Ikharia (they/them)
Emergency medicine doctor and TV presenter

Vulvas are not vaginas and vice versa

I honestly do not know what age I was when I realised that the world had been incorrectly naming my external genitalia. Even today, some folk think that the opposite of a penis is a vagina. So many of us owning vulvas refer to the area between our legs as our vaginas . . . WRONG!

Why is there a cohort of us doing this? Maybe it's because the word 'vulva' seems like an unpleasant mouthful? (Although personally I don't think the word 'penis' is that pleasant either!) Whatever our feelings are about how the words sound in our mouths, the bottom line is that it is imperative we are able to name and label our genitals CORRECTLY.

Let me roll things back a bit.

Do you remember the first ever label that you knowingly uttered for your external genitalia? Perhaps it was flower, nunny or Pum Pum? I think mine was 'private parts'. This feels more accurate than 'flower', which, if you ask me, sounds a bit patriarchal, as though it sets anyone with a vagina up to be 'deflowered' . . . ewww.

And what about now? Do you say vagina when you mean vulva, or do you still use the references you used as a child? Well, I'm here as a doc (trying to be as minimally patronising as possible btw) to empower you to resist incorrect labelling.

Vaginas are actually internal. The muscular birth canal, the area in which tampons sit, the space before your cervix: that's ya vagina. If you stand naked in front of the mirror you cannot see it.

The external area that grows hair (the part you do see) is a lump of flesh that sits over ya pubic bone called the mons pubis. It's a hairy cushion of fat and also NOT YOUR VAGINA.

If you trace your finger down your mons pubis you will come to a division which lead to ya labia – left and right. Collectively named ya labia majora. The skin here is like ya regular skin and has hair. Under ya labia majora is ya labia minora. The skin here is much like the lining of ya vagina, but with no muscle or hair. Ya labia can be symmetrical, asymmetrical, hang low, hang even, uneven – basically they come in many configurations.

All of these external parts make up ya vulva. NOT YOUR VAGINA.

I labour this point because one day something will feel, look or smell different in your genital region. You may need a smear test. You will have regular sexual health screenings. You may learn to touch yourself in ways that feel nice. And at some point you may have consensual sexual activity with someone else.

It is so important to me that anybody who has a vulva and vagina can accurately name what feels good or doesn't and can also recognise any changes. As an emergency medicine doctor, I see everything. I can't count the number of times that people have told me that they have an issue with their vagina and actually mean their vulva. And the number of times I've heard adults use the names of inanimate objects to describe their genitals . . . which can make my job pretty confusing!

Would it surprise you to learn that children are much better than adults at telling me and their parents what's what? In the emergency room I've looked after 7-year-olds who confidently tell me that they have caught the skin of their penis in their zippers, and kids who have fallen on the side of the bath while getting in and squashed their vulvas. These kids have obviously learned the correct terms, and that is so important. As a safety issue it is crucial that kids and young people correctly name their genitals with no shame.

In the same way you'd say 'that's my arm, it hurts', you should say 'this is my vulva, it hurts.'

I could go on and on and on about the importance of correctly naming our genitalia. I think some of our incorrect labelling or infantilisation of genitalia is wrapped up in a patriarchy that thrives on us being prudish. **Down with the patriarchy**: my vulva is not my vagina and vice versa!

Internal anatomy

Uterus/womb
The organ where foetuses grow. The uterus sometimes leans forward, sometimes is upright and sometimes leans back. Between puberty and menopause, it builds up a lining every 21–40 days in preparation for pregnancy. If no conception occurs, the lining is shed via a period.

Urethra
The urethra transports urine from your bladder to the outside world.

Pelvic floor
A layer of muscles that go across the bottom of your pelvic bone. Various tubes and organs pass through it, including the urethra, vagina and rectum.

Vagina
The organ where things such as period blood and babies come out, and things like fingers, penises, menstrual cups and the like go in. It can range from 4–14 cm. The inside of the vagina has accordion-like ridges called rugae.

Cervix
The cervix is a small doughnut-shaped muscle at the base of the uterus. The hole in the middle is for blood and babies to go out and sperm to go in. This is the bit that gets swabbed during a cervical screening.

Ovarian tube

The ovarian tube is like a highway for transporting an egg from the ovary to the uterus. It is often called the Fallopian tube. I don't like calling it that, though, as the guy it's named after is an Italian anatomist from the 1500s called Gabriele Falloppio. He once claimed to have 'discovered' the clitoris, but I think you'll find that everyone WITH a clitoris knew about it before the 16th century, thank you very much . . .

Ovary

Ovaries have two main functions: storing eggs and making hormones, including oestrogen, progesterone and testosterone.

Urethral sponge

A tube of spongy erectile tissue that surrounds the urethra. When you're aroused, it fills with blood, which compresses the urethra and makes it harder to pee during sex.

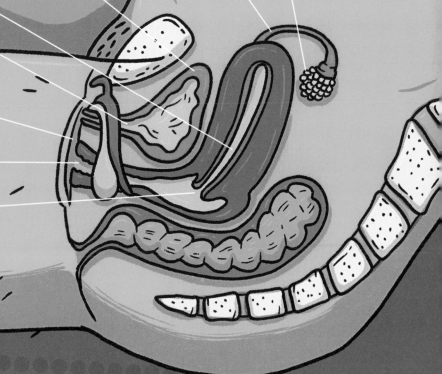

THE CLITORIS IS AN ICEBERG - THERE'S SO MUCH YOU CAN'T SEE UNDER THE SURFACE.

Clitoral anatomy

The clitoris is made of erectile tissue, so when you're sexually aroused, it fills up with blood and gets bigger and harder (just like a penis!). The glans clitoris is the only part of the clitoris that is on the outside of the body, the rest is referred to as the 'internal clitoris'.

Glans clitoris
Contains the highest concentration of nerves throughout the whole clitoris. It varies from 3–10 mm in width.

Body
The body is 13–59 mm in length.

Root
Connects the clitoral body to the crura.

Crus
The crus is 25–68 mm in length and sits behind the labia. The plural is crura.[6]

Vestibular bulb
The bulbs are 13–69 mm in length and 9–29 mm in width. They hug the end of the urethra and vagina.

Urethra and vagina
Not technically part of the clitoris, just nearby. As the clitoris, vagina and urethra are all located so closely to each other, they are sometimes lumped together and called the clitorourethrovaginal complex. Catchy . . .

> Somewhere, sometime, someone said that there are 8,000 nerves in the clitoris – double that of the penis. I have searched high and low for where this number came from and can find no source.

6   It's because it's Latin. Please don't ask me any more grammar questions.

I think we found the G-spot?!

The G-spot is a controversial part of the V. It's said to be an area on the front wall of the vagina (about 5–8 cm up) that, when stimulated, is very pleasurable. While some people are very adept at finding it, others search high and low to no avail, which has meant some people believe it doesn't exist . . .

It all started in 1950, when physician Dr Ernst Gräfenberg published a paper about this area based on reports from his patients. It has since been named the G-spot in his honour (patriarchy, eh?). Since then, no scientific study has revealed an organ, nerve bundle or anything previously undiscovered.

The only thing found in the area other than the urethra and vagina? The internal clitoris.

Here, my friends, is your big stonking clue. It's not even a clue – it's right there! Many, including myself, believe the G-spot is in fact the combination of the internal clitoris and the urethral sponge. They directly overlap with where the G-spot is supposed to be and are made of erectile tissue, which means stimulating them is pleasurable. Search over; put the map away; mystery solved– it was right in front of our eyes the whole time.

This might also explain why some people have a G-spot and some don't. The internal clitoris varies a lot in size and shape, so some people's internal clitoris may not be in the place needed to respond to G-spot stimulation.

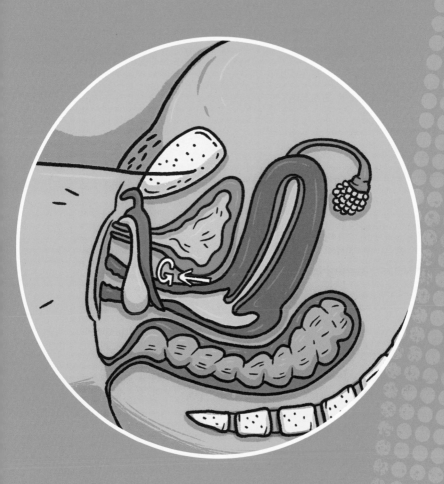

WHAT IS INTERSEX?

According to U.S. intersex advocacy organization interACT, 'intersex is an umbrella term for differences in sex traits or reproductive anatomy. Intersex people are born with these differences or develop them in adolescence. There are many possible differences in genitalia, hormones, internal anatomy or chromosomes compared to the usual two ways that human bodies develop.' (In other words, there are many possible differences that don't fit with the assumption that everyone is born with either a penis + XY chromosomes or a vagina + XX chromosomes). Some doctors call this 'disorders of sexual development' (DSD), but not everyone likes that term because it implies something is wrong with that person. I'm going to use intersex as it's currently the most widely accepted term.

Lots of people have parts that don't look like what you typically find in textbooks. And there are **loads** of different ways of being intersex. Examples include:

- **Mayer-Rokitansky-Küster-Hauser (MRKH) syndrome:** when a person has an average vulva and ovaries, but the vagina and uterus are not present or are underdeveloped.

- **Androgen insensitivity syndrome:** when a person has XY chromosomes, but their body doesn't respond to testosterone. They will have a vulva instead of a penis, and a vagina develops, but typically there is no uterus or cervix.

- **Congenital adrenal hyperplasia:** when a person has a larger-than-average clitoris due to very large adrenal glands (which are two glands that sit on top of the kidneys).

- **Klinefelter's Syndrome:** when a person has XXY

chromosomes. Symptoms vary and sometimes they are so mild, people don't even know they have it.

The Intersex Society of North America, which in the 1990s were one of the earliest online intersex advocacy organizations, described intersex as a 'socially constructed category that reflects real biological variation'. What does that mean exactly? Well, it means that all bodies are unique and where we draw the line between what makes the 'male' and 'female' sex is decided by societies. (We're going to explore this in further detail in chapter 8.)

Sex covers a number of factors, including chromosomes, gene expression, hormones, genitals and secondary sexual characteristics (such as breasts and beards). But – and this is a big but – the factors that comprise sex have been decided **by society**. And when trying to shove all these different factors into only two boxes, real people who don't fit exactly into either model get left outside. And because it is decided by society, many systems of oppression decide what counts as the 'correct way' to be a woman or a man, especially racism and ableism.

Here's a quick analogy: In Russian, the colour blue is actually two colours – there's light blue, called голубой (pronounced 'galuboy') and dark blue, called синий ('sinny'). Linguistically, they are two totally different colours – there's no way in Russian of just saying 'blue', as we do in English. That doesn't mean that blue looks any different when it's in Russia: it's the same colour, but they're just defining it differently. And it's exactly the same with sex. It's societies that have decided to create the categories 'male', 'female' and 'intersex', but that doesn't mean that you physically stop having a vulva or a penis when you don't fit exactly into one of these categories. These are **socially constructed ways** of understanding the human experience. And we need to take the lead from intersex activists on how to make the world a safer place for intersex people.

For various reasons, it's really difficult to determine exactly how many intersex people are living around the world. For example, not everyone agrees on the definition of intersex; some types of intersex aren't detectable without certain medical tests;[7] some types don't show up until later in life; and the big one: stigma.

There are surgeries, sometimes called 'normalization surgery' or 'intersex genital mutilation' (IGM) by activists. This is when a doctor performs surgery to change the appearance or assumed function of a child's clitoris, vagina, testes, urethra or other internal genital anatomy – generally because their genitals don't fit the textbook definitions or images. This is never a surgery that is related to saving a child's life. Surgery is typically done on babies and children. It often causes more harm than good and can cause pain, a loss of physical sensitivity, emotional trauma and, in some cases, difficulties giving birth later down the line. It's not an overstatement to say that performing genital surgery on healthy children is a human rights violation. IGM is currently only banned or restricted in Chile, Colombia, Germany, Malta and Tamil Nadu, India. Such significant surgery should be decided by the person receiving it, at an age when they can make an informed decision.

Because of all these factors, the data can be pretty sketchy, but the best estimate we have is that 1.7 per cent of the human population is intersex. To put that in context, that means there are currently 132 million people in the world who are estimated to be intersex.

THAT'S ROUGHLY THE POPULATION OF MEXICO

7 Medical testing for intersex variations is extremely controversial, as it can lead to stigma and discrimination, especially when these tests are done in uterus and can lead to abortions of wanted and healthy foetuses.

Breaking the hymen myth

Public conversation around the hymen is rife with myths and stigma. Loving your V requires being able to bust these myths and separate the fact from the fiction. Let's do some fact-checking of some common (and very wrong) myths about the infamous hymen together:

Question: What does the hymen look like?
Answer: The hymen is a skirt of skin round the edge of the vagina with a big hole in the middle for things to go in and out.

It's a common myth that the hymen is like a tamper-proof seal covering the vagina. But think about it: if the hymen totally covered the vagina, how would period blood come out before you've had sex? The hymen is actually a flap of skin round the edge of the vaginal opening and is variable in shape and size.

And, like all skin, it's very pliable and elastic. The vast majority of people have a hymen like this, and it doesn't restrict access to the vagina.

On very rare occasions, a person is born with a hymen that does completely cover the vagina. This is called an imperforate hymen and is usually spotted at birth or during puberty. This can make penetration painful and disrupt menstruation. Doctors usually surgically remove or reduce the size of imperforate hymens with a minor surgery called a hymenectomy.

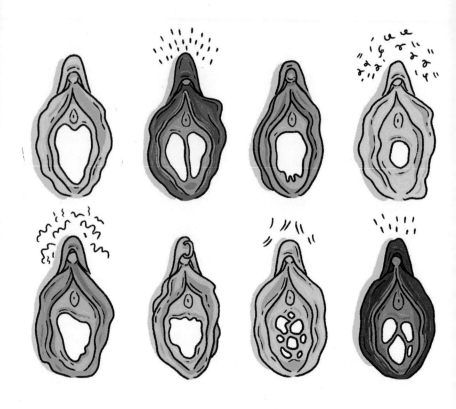

Question: What does the hymen do?

Answer: No one knows why the hymen exists, but we do know it serves no function in relation to sex.

Major myth incoming! A commonplace myth goes that the hymen 'breaks' the first time you have sex. TOTES FALSE. Tissue can handle being pushed around a bit – that's kind of its whole deal. You'd have to do some damage to make tissue tear. The hymen can usually handle vaginal penetration – including by tampons – with no injury. The hymen isn't fragile like tissue paper nor so brittle it snaps like crunchy leaves. It's elastic skin just like the rest of your vulva and it gets more elastic as you age.

If you do experience bleeding or pain during sex, it's almost never to do with the hymen and is usually due to a lack of lubrication or not being aroused enough yet. Bleeding or pain during sex can also be due to a medical condition, and if this happens to you, arrange a doctor's visit. And despite the rumours, lots of people have vaginal sex for the first time without bleeding or pain. I did!

Question: What can a hymen tell you about a person?
Answer: Basically, nothing.

There's a big misconception that you can tell if someone has had sex from the way their hymen looks. Skin can tear, but it's not like you can look at a hymen and see some big scar with graffiti that says 'penis woz here'. Hymens are super variable in shape, colour and texture. It's almost impossible to spot any changes to your hymen after having penetrative vaginal sex for the first time. And some people are even born without a hymen at all! Around the world, some people have been subject to virginity testing, which is when someone's vulva is examined to determine if they are a virgin. This was only made illegal in the UK in 2021. But as

you now know, it's exceptionally inaccurate, and a total violation. There's literally no information you can glean about someone's sexual history by looking at a vulva.

Why do these myths persist? You're going to start spotting a theme because the answer's often the same: the kyriarchy (see page 9).

There has been a push to rename the hymen because the word has such patriarchal connotations. Swedish organization RFSU suggested 'vaginal corona' (or, in Swedish, *slidkrans*, which literally translates as 'vaginal garland') because corona means 'crown/wreath' in Latin and the hymen looks a bit like a wreath round the vagina. But if you lived through 2020, you'll know why I think it's doubtful anything with 'corona' in the name will catch on. Can you think of a new, more feminist word for the hymen?

The pelvic floor: how to exercise without leaving your bed

A healthy and strong pelvic floor is important for three main reasons:

1 It helps prevent incontinence (i.e. it stops you weeing/ pooing involuntarily).

2 It helps prevent the organs in the pelvis, such as the uterus, bladder or bowel, from slipping downwards from their usual position (this is called pelvic organ prolapse).

3 When you have sex or masturbate, you might experience an orgasm. Stronger pelvic floor = better orgasms!

To have a strong pelvic floor, you need to exercise![8] You might have heard pelvic floor exercises being called Kegel exercises or just Kegels. Dr Arnold Kegel, an American gynaecologist, theorized in the 1940s that if other muscles in the body could be strengthened through exercises, the same should be true of the pelvic floor. He invented a 'perineometer' – an instrument that goes inside the vagina that you squeeze as hard as you can. A dial shows you how hard you're able to squeeze – like those strength testers at funfairs, only instead of winning a teddy, you win an exercise regime.

How do you do these exercises? First, you need to understand how to consciously use your pelvic muscles. Let's try it now! Do

8   Some people, such as those who experience vaginismus, have pelvic floors that contract too much. In such cases these pelvic floor exercises **won't help**, so it's better to speak to a physiotherapist to get recommendations on more appropriate exercises to help your pelvic floor relax.

that thing where you want to stop peeing mid flow – you know that muscle you just clenched? That's your pelvic floor!

Here are some exercises you can do. Try to do one set of each exercise type three times a day:

Sustained contraction

Clench your pelvic floor and hold it for a few seconds. Then relax the muscles. When relaxing, do it gently and in a controlled way until it's totally relaxed. Clench and relax ten times – that's one set. Start off by trying to clench for five seconds, then release for five seconds, and over time work upwards until you can hold for ten seconds.

Quick flicks

Tighten and relax your pelvic floor quickly ten times – that's one set. Each clench and release should take just a second.

It can take a few weeks of doing this every day to see improvements in your pelvic floor strength. If you are worried about your pelvic floor for any reason, it's always best to speak to your GP – the advice in this book isn't a substitute for seeing a doctor!

TOP TIPS:

- Keep your butt, thighs and abdomen relaxed while doing the exercises.

- Don't hold your breath.

- Don't worry if you can't do it for more than a few seconds. It takes time to build up strength.

- Grab a mirror and have a look while doing your exercises. If you're doing it right, you see your urethra 'winking' at you.

- The relaxing is just as important as the clenching part. You need to be able to relax those muscles or they will get too used to staying contracted, which is also no good.

- If you're the type to forget to do your exercises (been there), the NHS has an app called Squeezy that'll make you an exercise plan, send notifications and help track your progress.

- If you're based in England, there are also pelvic health physiotherapists available on the NHS who can help you to make sure you're completing the exercises correctly.

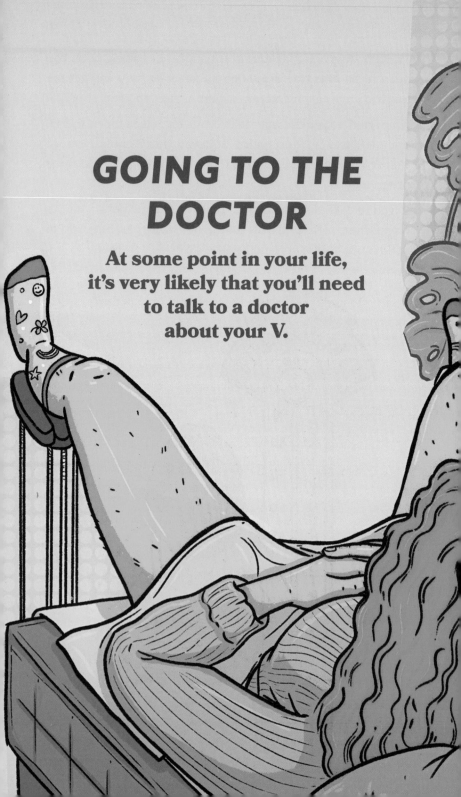

GOING TO THE DOCTOR

At some point in your life, it's very likely that you'll need to talk to a doctor about your V.

Now you're armed with the foundational knowledge we've covered in this chapter, this is hopefully a bit less daunting. For instance, if you have a pain in your vulva, you will know to tell your doctor that your vulva hurts, rather than your vagina, meaning the doctor won't end up poking around in the vaginal canal for no reason (which happens a lot more than you might realize).

To help make this experience easier for you, I've put together some tips so you can be prepared.

Talking to a medical professional

A doctor or other medical professional definitely has more knowledge (unless you're a medical professional yourself, obvs), but no one knows how you feel better than you. Everyone is unique and only you know what's normal for you. Be your own advocate! Here are some tips on how to communicate effectively:

- Be specific about your symptoms. Rather than just 'uncomfortable', can you describe what you're feeling as throbbing, stabbing, itching, burning or something else?

- Be specific about the location. Is it a large or small area? If you're not comfortable with showing it on your body, you can bring an illustration of a vulva and point it out on that.

- Be specific about the time. Have you been experiencing a symptom for a day, a week, months, years?

- Be prepared to answer questions about your medical history, such as other conditions, past treatments, medications you're on or family history.

- Do you have any accompanying mental health issues, such as anxiety or depression? It's not just physical health problems that you can seek professional help with.

- You can suggest a diagnosis, but also let your doctor explore other options as there might be something you haven't considered.

- Don't be afraid to ask questions and take notes. You are allowed to be an active participant in your care!

- If you feel like your concerns are being dismissed, ask your doctor for a 'differential diagnosis'. This is basically a list of all the possible things that could be causing your symptoms. Then ask your doctor how they've ruled out the things on that list. This should force your doctor to take your symptoms seriously and investigate further.[9]

- If they are doing a physical examination of your body and it's painful, you can always ask them to stop.

- Don't put up with them if they make you feel uncomfortable or judged. If something doesn't feel right, tell them.

- Read up about the V from trusted sources (such as this book!) to get some foundational knowledge.

STI screening

A sexually transmitted infection, or STI, is predominantly passed on through sexual contact with another person with the infection.[10] Some display symptoms, while others are symptomless. Many have implications if left untreated, so it's important to get screened regularly and receive prompt treatment. A screening is when you are tested for a disease even if there are no symptoms, to catch it early. These tests could be in the form of a swab or a blood test. You can do some at home, but some must be done by a professional.[11]

---

9 Thank you to Dorender Dankwa on TikTok for this amazing strategy.

10 Some STIs can also be passed on through other types of contact such as breastfeeding, pregnancy or blood exposure.

11 I definitely wouldn't want to take my own blood!

How often you get screened depends on your lifestyle. If you are sexually active, get tested at least once a year. If you are having unprotected sex or have multiple partners, then consider doing it every three or six months. Your doctor or nurse will be able to advise how often is enough for you. For more information about STIs, please see page 125–126.

Cervical smears

Cervical smears are a type of screening to check your cervix's health. In the UK, you'll be offered a cervical screening when you turn 25, but this age differs in countries around the world. You'll then be offered one every 1–5 years (depending on a bunch of different factors, such as your age or other health conditions) until you are in your mid-60s or if your cervix is surgically removed.

When your screening is due, you'll usually receive a letter from your GP inviting you to make an appointment. If you don't receive this when you're at the right age, call them. You should have one even if you aren't sexually active.

The whole appointment usually only takes ten minutes max and this is what you can expect:

1   The doctor or nurse will ask you to go behind a little curtain and take your underwear off.

2   You lie down on the bed with your legs spread apart. Sometimes there are little rests to put your feet on.

3   The person doing the smear will put some lubricant on a speculum (a tool for looking inside orifices) and put it inside your vagina to open it. Sometimes the speculums are cold, but you can ask for the speculum to be run under warm water for a few seconds first. Speculums come in different sizes, so if you find it particularly uncomfortable, you can ask them to use a smaller one.

There's no reason to use a bigger one, no matter the size of your vagina.

4 They'll move the speculum around a bit to find your cervix.

5 When they find it, they'll insert a little swab and move it across the edge of your cervix. Sometimes you can feel it, and sometimes you can't. It might feel like a little scratch, but it shouldn't be any more painful than that.

6 They'll take the swab out, followed by the speculum, then send it to a lab for testing. You'll usually get the results by post or phone.

What if I'm uncomfortable during the screening?

If you experience discomfort at any time, tell the person doing the smear and ask for any adjustments you need. They want to make sure it isn't an unpleasant experience for you because they want you to keep coming back and not be afraid of the screenings.

Does it hurt?

It shouldn't! A small percentage of people find speculums painful. This could either be because the person using it isn't being gentle enough or is not using lubricant or due to certain medical conditions such as vaginismus.

Also, some people who have experienced sexual assault can find pelvic exams re-traumatizing. If this is the case for you, discuss this with the person doing the exam so you can work together to find the best way to proceed. You don't have to tell them what happened, just that using the speculum may be difficult for you.

What should I wear?

Whatever you want! I personally find wearing a long skirt comforting because it makes me feel less 'naked' to just pull my skirt up instead of taking my trousers completely off. I like wearing my favourite socks to have something fun to look at during the smear.

Should I shave my pubic hair?

Honestly, the person doing the smear won't even notice, so do whatever you want with your pubic hair. I used to be a nursing assistant, and I can tell you from experience that you get really desensitized to nakedness when you're looking at genitals for 12 hours a day. They honestly won't care what your vulva looks or smells like.

What to do if you have a bad doctor or nurse

The sad truth is that although we want to be able to trust all medical professionals, there are some people who do or say upsetting things – whether that's ignoring their patient's symptoms, underestimating their pain, being judgemental, body-shaming them or being straight up rude or dismissive. Medical professionals are human and will make mistakes, but that's not an excuse – they have a responsibility to do better.

There is always an avenue to complain about your medical provider. Find the organization that awards their licence in your country, and you can speak to them about your experience. Then find a new medical practitioner. Trust me: when you find a good one it's such a great feeling. Good doctors and nurses – ones that make you feel listened to and truly cared for – do exist; it's just sometimes they're the second person you see.

RACISM IN MEDICINE

Gynaecology, like many other branches of medicine, has a racist history. There have been many doctors, surgeons and medical professionals who have done unspeakable things. For example, Dr. J. Marion Sims – known as the 'father of gynaecology' – developed his pioneering surgical techniques by experimenting on enslaved Black women in the 1800s. By caring more about the results of his experiments than the well-being of the enslaved women (who were not able to give consent to this treatment due to their position), he would have caused unimaginable suffering to the women. This history still affects us today in many tangible ways, and we continue to see this discrimination in healthcare systems across the world.[12] There are many other examples throughout history and in the present day that I could mention, but fortunately many fantastic organizations round the world – such as Sister Song and Decolonising Contraception – are working to combat racism in medicine and support reproductive justice.

12 To explore the subject in more detail, I would recommend reading *Medical Bondage: Race, Gender, and the Origins of American Gynecology* by Deirdre Cooper Owens.

FATPHOBIA IN MEDICINE

Our health is complicated. Yet so often our health is reduced to one factor: weight. But it's totally possible to be thin and ill, or fat and healthy. And if you are fat and ill, losing weight is very rarely a factor in becoming healthy again – nor is being thin a reliable way to cure your ill health. Even the way we measure fatness is broken. BMI doesn't take into account that muscle weighs more than fat – so it would classify many athletes as 'overweight' and unhealthy!

When people make negative assumptions about people who are fat and discriminate against them, this is fatphobia. It is rife in medicine and too many people are told to lose weight before they can receive proper medical care – even when their symptoms are totally unrelated to weight. When a doctor sees 'fat' before they see 'person', health conditions get missed. This is hugely important for gynaecological care, as things like a swollen abdomen can be symptomatic of serious gynaecological diseases. Fatphobia must end – we deserve to live in a world where all people are treated with compassion, regardless of what their body looks like.

Now you're a vulva expert

Talking just about gynaecological anatomy and health could fill up a whole book, and yet there is still so much we don't know. This field has been massively ignored by funders and researchers. In 2014, £48 million was spent in the UK on researching reproductive health and childbirth. It sounds like a lot, until you realize that figure represents only 2.3 per cent of all the money spent on medical research that year. Considering 31 per cent of people with vulvas have experienced severe reproductive health symptoms, this seems pretty out of balance.

It's not fair and it's not right.
We must demand change!

But you now have a beautiful thing: knowledge. I am officially awarding you the 'vulva-expert' badge. Go you! This knowledge will be the foundation for all the things to come in this book, and you can come back and refer to it whenever you need to. It's information such as this that can help you take charge of your health, smash stigma and misinformation, and truly celebrate a magnificent part of the body. And to be perfectly honest? You have a RIGHT to know about your body.

YOU DESERVE THIS.
END OF.

Chapter 2
THE CYCLE OF LIFE

Our bodies are in a constant state of change. It's absolutely mind-blowing. And if you have a body with a V, like mine, there's a specific journey you'll probably go on:

MENARCHE
(THE FIRST PERIOD)

MENSTRUATION

MENOPAUSE
(WHEN YOU STOP HAVING PERIODS)

Ahh, the three Ms. Some people go through this journey a little faster, some a little slower and some take a completely different path. We're going to explore that journey – why it happens; some of the forks in the road that you might take; a little science; a little history; and a few personal stories dotted in there because sometimes you've just gotta do some oversharing.

I want to preface this chapter by saying that at the end of the day, you do YOU. If I had a life motto, it would be that.

- If you want to make your own reusable period pad when you're on your period – go for it!

- If you feel more comfortable using tampons – that's perfect!

- If you want to have a baby when you're ready – that's fricking cool.

- If you don't want to use your body to make a baby – that's also fricking cool, and I admire you for knowing what you want and doing it. (And of course, there are also loads of things that get in the way of that journey that we have no control over, such as infertility or ill health.)

There are tons of amazing things we can do with our bodies that are not reproduction-centred, and I wholeheartedly believe those should be seen as equally valuable.

It would be an honour to take you on this journey with me. Going through this cycle is probably a very time-consuming part of your life if you have a V (I mean, periods literally happen every month, which is way too often if you ask me, and I would like to speak to nature's manager).

But because this is such a big part of your life, knowing how your V works and some of the things that happen to it is the best way to acknowledge your power and live life in a way that works for you. Celebrating your V is way easier when you understand its workings – and just how incredible it is.

Bleeding for a week without dying is metal AF

I remember one day in primary school when the boys were all sent to one room and the girls another. The boys learnt about how their armpits were going to get smelly and grow hair, and us girls learnt about how we were going to bleed from our vaginas every month for the next 40 years. Oh, and also our armpits will get smelly too. The awkward teacher doing sex ed decided it was time for us to learn how to use a pad, so she whipped out some knickers from her bag, unwrapped a pad and stuck it on, holding it up high so everyone could see. Suddenly, a boy was spotted peering through the window of the door. We all giggled, but the teacher was mortified and quickly shooed him away for a stern talking-to.

That was the day I learnt that I was expected to be ashamed of my period. That it was a thing men were supposed to ignore and women were supposed to whisper about.

But what is there to be ashamed of? Periods are normal and natural, and should be treated as such. Saying you're on your period should be no more remarkable than saying what you're planning to wear today or what TV show you're watching.

Yet 37 per cent of people who menstruate in the UK have experienced period-shaming, and – even more horrifyingly – 40 per cent of those people said the shaming came from their partner. This shaming can lead to numerous day-to-day challenges, such as feeling like you need to hide your pad when carrying it to the toilet. But the shaming can also lead to far more heartbreaking occurrences. In Nepal in 2010, an 11-year-old girl died after she was sent to live in a shed during her period, in a practice called छाउपडी, or *chhaupadi*, which is when people who are menstruating are banned from the house and participating in the community. When this girl fell ill while in the shed during her period, her family refused to take her to the hospital because touching her while she was menstruating would make them 'impure'. This girl's experience and my own are worlds apart in terms of severity, but at the heart of them is the same idea that we should be ashamed of our periods.

But why should periods even raise an eyebrow? Literally, why? If someone finds them gross, that's a them-problem, not a you-problem.

A person with a uterus will have on average 480 periods in their lifetime. That's about 2,400 days of bleeding. It's simply how our body works. Treating it like something that should only be spoken about in hushed tones doesn't help anyone.

In fact, celebrating periods would be far more helpful! Shout about them from the rooftops, if you want to! Grab a bullhorn and climb to the top of the nearest tall building and tell everyone passing by, 'I'm bleeding from my vagina!!!' Call me – I'll come join you. Next time you feel embarrassed about your perfectly natural period (though I hope you won't have a 'next time' after reading this book), think of me sitting next to you telling you how bloody powerful I think it is that you bleed once a month and you don't die. **That's metal AF.**

Muffbusters

**Let's sort out some myths
before we get started:**

- Period blood ISN'T dirty or disgusting. It's totally normal and natural.

- People DON'T sync up their cycles when they live together. This is one myth I wish were true. Think of the power! Sadly, there's little scientific proof this happens, and it's probably just a coincidence. Seeing as we menstruate roughly once a month for up to seven days, there's going to be overlap sometimes.

- You CAN get pregnant on your period. Sperm can live inside your body for up to five days, so if you have a short cycle and if someone ejaculates inside you near the end of your period, it absolutely could coincide with your next ovulation.

- Using an inserted menstrual product WON'T 'take your virginity'. That's not how virginity works (see pages 90–91).

- Sharks WON'T attack you if you swim in the sea while on your period. I have not been able to find a single instance of a shark attacking someone who was menstruating.

How the menstrual cycle works

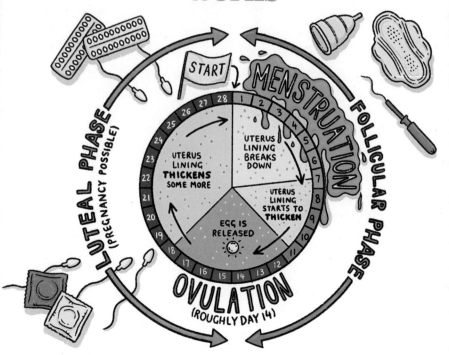

START

MENSTRUATION

FOLLICULAR PHASE

LUTEAL PHASE (PREGNANCY POSSIBLE)

UTERUS LINING BREAKS DOWN

UTERUS LINING **THICKENS** SOME MORE

UTERUS LINING STARTS TO **THICKEN**

EGG IS RELEASED

OVULATION (ROUGHLY DAY 14)

Day 1: Menstruation

Day one of the menstrual cycle is the first day of your period – when the lining of the uterus is shed. Bleeding lasts on average for three to seven days. You lose around 30–50ml of menstrual fluid per period. Menstrual fluid is made up of blood, cells from the endometrium (the lining of the uterus), vaginal discharge and cervical mucus.

First half of cycle: Follicular phase (pre-ovulation)

The brain makes a hormone that prompts the brain to make another hormone that prompts the making of ANOTHER hormone that tells the ovary to get ready for ovulation. It's like a big game of Telephone that takes a couple weeks. The follicle (the sac that contains the egg) makes oestrogen, which prompts the uterus lining to thicken.

Day 7ish: Proliferative phase

The hormone oestrogen prompts a new lining to be built up to replace the one just lost.

Day 14ish: Ovulation

Once oestrogen levels reach a certain point, ovulation happens. This is when the egg leaves the ovary to start its journey down the ovarian tube towards the uterus.

Second half of cycle: Luteal phase (post ovulation)

The egg travels down the ovarian tube, leaving behind it a little empty sac it used to live in, called the corpus luteum.

Day 18ish: Secretory phase

The corpus luteum produces the hormone progesterone, which keeps the lining of the uterus thick. If the egg isn't fertilized, the corpus luteum shrinks and stops making progesterone.[13] This means the uterus lining isn't getting the signal to be maintained, so the lining is shed – a period! The purpose of the thick lining is to support a fertilized egg at the beginning of its development. So if there is no fertilized egg, the lining breaks down. Then we're back at square one! This cycle can take anywhere from 21 to 40 days.

---

13   If the egg is fertilized, it will secrete the chemical hCG (this is what pregnancy tests detect). It tells the corpis luteum to keep going until the placenta is ready to take over making progesterone

Want to track your period?

It's a great way of learning more about yourself, such as how your body and emotions change with your cycle; when you are at your most fertile; how long your cycle tends to last; and helps you spot if you're late or if you've missed a period. You can do it with an old-fashioned paper calendar just by marking Xs on the days you've bled or – if you don't want to do the maths, like me – there are loads of apps you can get. Some are free and some are paid for, but I'd definitely recommend one with a robust data-protection policy.

Don't cramp my style

Everyone's experience of periods is different – some people barely notice them; and for others, it's a stay-in-bed-all-day affair. Symptoms can also change with age – lots of people have terrible cramps when they are a teenager that get milder once they are in their twenties. Taking hormonal contraception also changes symptoms – annoyingly, it can either make them better or worse, and you won't know until you begin to use it.

The symptoms you get around your menstrual cycle are often called PMS, which stands for premenstrual syndrome. It's called 'premenstrual', but these symptoms can happen any time during the cycle. Confusing. It's almost impossible to get reliable data on PMS because scientists can't agree on what the definitive symptoms are.

There are literally dozens of different symptoms associated with periods, including sore breasts, bloating, acne, spots, headaches, mouth ulcers, bloating, appetite changes and mood swings. There are many more, and to list them all here would take pages and pages, so I've included some of the most common ones on the next couple of pages.

Period pain

Abdominal pains happen because your uterus is contracting to help shed its lining. A group of chemicals called pro-staglandins spur on these contractions, which temporarily restrict blood flow. This then decreases the oxygen supply, which sets off alarm bells in your cells and causes pain. Your uterus squeezes itself so hard it hurts itself. Babe, same.

There are lots of different ways to relieve period pain:

- Painkillers (ibuprofen and aspirin have been shown to work better than paracetamol for cramps).

- A hot-water bottle or a hot bath.

- Light exercise such as cycling, walking or swimming. The endorphins you get from exercise are literally a painkiller your body produces itself.

- Doing things that make you happy, like watching your favourite movie or eating your favourite food.

- Massaging your abdomen.

- A TENS machine – this is a little machine that delivers a small electrical current.

- Hormonal birth control. For some people, period pain is so bad that the best option is to even out the hormone cycle so they don't get those highs and lows.

- Having an orgasm – whether that is through solo sex or with a partner if you are sexually active – can reduce period pain.

Changes in sex drive

Our sex drive – or libido – can be super sensitive, getting turned down by things such as stress and pain, and turned up by hormones or the increased physical sensitivity that comes with periods. That's why on your period it really could go either way. (We'll cover sex drive in more detail on page 102–103.)

Lethargy

Your body is going through a lot – building uterus linings, getting rid of them, managing hormones – so tiredness is to be expected. If you look online for more information about tiredness during periods, what comes up is usually how to fight it with exercise or something else. But I'm going to give you some pretty radical advice: embrace it. Rest is a revolutionary act in a world where we're constantly expected to be doing everything all the time. The human body needs rest. You deserve rest, especially during your period.

Diarrhoea and constipation

Remember those pesky prostaglandins that cause your uterus to contract? Well, they do the same to your bowel, which causes the dreaded period runs. On the other hand, you can also get constipation on your period – no one knows why, but it's probably got something to do with oestrogen or progesterone. The body is confusing.

Vulva congestion

This is basically soreness or a feeling of 'fullness' in your vulva due to the extra blood flowing in this part of the body.

Code red

Sometimes period symptoms require more than just a painkiller and an early night. If your period feels like the gates of hell have opened up in your belly and loads of tiny demons are poking at your insides with those giant fork things, speak to a doctor.

Here are some things to keep an eye on and some suggestions about what might be causing them to discuss with your doctor:

Very painful periods

Period pain is very common, but it shouldn't be so bad that you can't physically move because it feels like a pack of chihuahuas are using your insides as a chew toy. Extreme period pain could be caused by conditions such as endometriosis, adenomyosis, pelvic inflammatory disease or fibroids. If you feel that your period pain is being dismissed by doctors, I recommend pushing the issue if it's something that is concerning you. In the UK, it takes an average of seven and a half years to get a diagnosis of endometriosis. This is unfair, so push for the care you deserve.

Irregular periods

When you first start menstruating, it can take a few years to settle into a regular cycle, and even then some people are just a bit more irregular than others. Periods are really sensitive to general health and well-being, so your cycle length can change because of loads of things.

Common causes of irregular periods can be stress, weight changes, starting a new contraception, polycystic ovary syndrome

(PCOS), perimenopause, or medical conditions putting a toll on your body. Obviously, some of these causes are completely normal and irregularity is expected. But in some cases, you might need to speak to a doctor. The first step is to start tracking your cycle, and you should see a medical professional if:

- Your periods last longer than seven days.

- You had a regular period, and then suddenly it became irregular, but this can't be explained by something such as perimenopause or starting a new contraception.

- You have periods more often than every 21 days, or less often than every 40 days.

- You're bleeding between periods.

Heavy bleeding

Menorrhagia is very heavy or prolonged bleeding when you're on your period, and I do mean **heavy**. Like waking-up-and-your-bed-looks-like-a-murder-scene heavy. Heavy bleeding can be caused by a variety of things, such as fibroids, endometriosis, adenomyosis, uterine cancer or PCOS. In some people, no underlying cause is found – I guess Mother Nature just likes to pick on people sometimes. What counts as heavy will vary between people, but generally you should look out for:

- Changing your period product more often than it says on the packaging.

- Regularly bleeding through your clothes even when you're using a menstrual product.

- Passing blood clots larger than a 10p coin.

- Needing to use more than one product together to manage the flow, such as a tampon and a pad.

Stopped or missed periods

It can be alarming if your periods suddenly stop. Your first thought might be pregnancy or menopause, but it could also be stress, hormonal contraception, sudden weight changes, doing too much exercise or PCOS. See a doctor if you miss more than three periods in a row and you have a negative pregnancy test.

Early or delayed periods

Most people start their periods aged 12, but it can happen anywhere between 10 and 16. I got mine when I was 11 because I like to get ahead of the game. If it happens before 10 years old, it can be a sign of an underlying medical condition, which should be investigated. If your periods still haven't started by 16, get it checked out. It could be due to being underweight, stress, an underlying medical condition, doing too much exercise or an intersex condition. In some cases, puberty blockers are used to delay puberty until that person's body and mind are ready.

PMDD

PMDD (premenstrual dysphoric disorder) is basically really intense PMS during which the symptoms have a much bigger impact on your life. I'm not talking about being a bit weepy when the shop doesn't have your favourite chocolate in stock – I'm talking extreme mood swings, suicidal feelings, depression, anxiety and the physical symptoms of PMS but dialled up to 11. Because of this, sometimes PMDD is classified as a hormone condition and sometimes a mental health condition. Depending on your symptoms, there are different treatment strategies that your doctor should be able to talk you through.

How ~not~ to
have blood on your hands

There are so many different kinds of menstrual products out there, sometimes I just want to take the choice out and free bleed (not use a menstrual product at all – i.e. probably what most people did for the vast majority of history). But I also don't want to do that much washing.

There are loads of different factors to consider and you have to pick what's best for you. Your preferred method may also change depending on what's going on in your life, so don't be afraid to try something new once in a while. You could also use a mix of methods – for example, if you're a bit anxious using a reusable method when you're out, you can use them at home and switch to disposables while out.

If there were any methods I would advise against, they would be sea sponges and home-made reusable tampons. Any menstrual product going inside your vagina has to be sterilized to be safe. Sea sponges are actual living organisms that used to live in the sea before being inserted into the vagina. Sterilizing them is very difficult, and the same goes for home-made tampons too.

Here are some factors that you'll need to consider when picking what's right for you:

- The heaviness of your period.
- What feels comfortable.
- How active you are.
- Whether the product is disposable or reusable.
- Access to cleaning facilities.
- Environmental sustainability.
- Affordability.

In many countries around the world, period products are classed as 'non-essential items', so are taxed at a higher rate – usually called a 'tampon tax'. Totally ridiculous! Period products are unquestionably essential items, and there have been many protests round the world to get rid of these taxes. In Germany, a period-product manufacturer called The Female Company found a loophole in the law – since tampons were usually taxed at 19 per cent but books at 7 per cent, they produced *The Tampon Book* – a short book about periods that contained a set of tampons on its last page. In January 2020, the fight was successful and the tax on menstrual products was reduced to 7 per cent – the same rate as essential items such as food and bus tickets.

Disposable pads/pantyliners

A disposable pad is probably the first period product you'll use. They are usually made from rayon or plastic. Pantyliners are thinner and can be used on really light days or to protect against tampon leaks.

Reusable pads/pantyliners

These are like a disposable pad but made of fabric. You can buy them from a shop or make one yourself! There's instructions later on if you want to try making one. If you need to change pads while you're out, bring a waterproof bag (or just a resealable freezer bag) to store the old pad until you get home.

Period underwear

These are knickers or underpants that have an absorbent section in the gusset. You can use them as the main absorber for your blood or wear them as a backup for a tampon or cup in case it leaks.

Tampons

Tampons are one of the most common period products. A tampon is a cylinder of absorbent material with a string on the end, which expands when it soaks up blood. Some come with applicators that are disposable or you can get reusable ones. When you put them in properly, you shouldn't be able to feel that they're there.

Menstrual cups and discs

A menstrual cup is a little silicone or rubber cup with a stem at the bottom that is inserted in the vagina. A disc is very similar but sits higher up in the vagina and doesn't have the little stem that cups have. They collect blood that you then pour down the toilet. Like tampons, if inserted properly, you shouldn't be able to feel it's there. It's the only method where you can see what your blood really looks like, which I think is pretty cool. However, if you have an IUD (see pages 118–119), you'll need to be extra careful taking them out! It's very important that you allow the suction pressure to be released before you pull out the menstrual cup, to avoid causing any harm.

You might have heard of something called Toxic Shock Syndrome (TSS), which is a life-threatening bacterial infection historically associated with tampons. It's actually really rare – fewer than 0.01 per cent of people who menstruate will get it a year.

The reason menstrual TSS is so high profile is because in the 1970s a new tampon called the Rely tampon was made, and it was actually too good at absorbing. Because of this, it was a breeding ground for bacteria. It disproportionately caused TSS, and it was famously pulled from the shelves because of it. Modern tampons don't have this problem.

Some people claim that it's better to use tampons with unbleached cotton, as the bleaching leaves traces of a chemical called dioxin. Dioxin is a toxic chemical and a widespread pollutant. But here's the thing – you eat about 13,000–240,000 times more dioxin than you are putting in your vagina with a tampon. It's important to know how your menstrual products are made to ensure they are safe, but know that bleached tampons will not harm you. If you're worried about this pollutant, you're better off telling members of your government to get off their arses and deal with the widespread environmental destruction caused by capitalism.[14]

14 Again, that's a story for another book.

DISPOSABLES OR REUSABLE MENSTRUAL PRODUCTS?

DISPOSABLES,
e.g. tampons and disposable pads

REUSABLES,
e.g. reusable pads, period underwear, menstrual cups/discs

PROS
- Cheap in the short term.
- Small, so they don't take up too much room in a bag or pocket.
- Can be bought in most shops.

PROS
- Cheaper in the long run.
- Much less wasteful.
- Don't need to be changed very often.

CONS
- Very wasteful.
- Need to be changed more frequently.

CONS
- You need to remember to wash them between uses.
- Start-up costs can be expensive.
- You'll need access to clean water to change them, and a place to dry them too.

Menstrual products and the environment

If you use only disposable period products throughout your life, how many in total are going into the bin? Let's do some rough maths.

(((4 day tampons + 1 night one) x 5 days in a period) x 13 periods a year) x 36 years of menstruation = 11,700 tampons going in the bin in one lifetime.

Disposable menstrual products contain a lot of plastic, which takes hundreds of years to decompose. If you flush them down the toilet, they can end up in our oceans, shedding microplastics and being eaten by sea life – pads and tampon applicators are some of the most common types of rubbish polluting our oceans. We only have one Earth, and it's our collective responsibility to look after it. A truly helpful thing you can do is use reusable period products.

However, it's equally important to be mindful that not everyone can use reusable menstrual products. This could be because of cost; access to private hygiene facilities; or a health condition, so never pressure anyone into using something they aren't able to. There are also loads of other things you can do, such as:

- Support local environmental activists and campaigns.

- Write to manufacturers encouraging them to use more sustainable materials in their products.

- Ask your local shops to stock reusable menstrual products.

- Ask your school to include discussions about reusables in sex and relationships education sessions.

- Contact your local representative and encourage them to use their power to prevent further pollution and clean up our planet.

- Make reusable pads for yourself or to give to your friends.

Together we can protect our planet and still have a bloody great period!

How to make your own reusable pad

Making your own pad is so easy! There's loads of ways to do it and this one is just a suggestion – a quick search on the internet will reveal other methods for making a reusable pad if this one doesn't work for you. When choosing fabrics, try to choose ones with natural fibres, as synthetic fabrics often shed microplastics, which pollute our water.

You will need:

- Needle

- Thread

- Pins or clips to hold fabric in place while you sew.

- Scissors

- Something to mark the fabric, such as chalk or a pen.

- A thin fabric for the wrap, such as cotton, jersey, fleece or hemp – a great opportunity for upcycling old clothes or pillowcases.

- A thick, absorbent fabric for the liner, such as flannel, fleece, terry cloth or an old towel. To test if it will be a good fabric, splash some water on it – your fabric should absorb it immediately instead of the water beading on the top.

- Optional: a waterproof fabric for lining the pad e.g. PUL, fabric from a raincoat or broken umbrella.

- Paper and a pen for making the pattern.

- Something to hold the wings together, such as a button or poppers.

Instructions

1 Trace the shape on this page on to a piece of paper, then cut it out. You can make it longer, shorter, wider or thinner to fit your body better.

2 Using your paper cut-out as a guide, cut two copies of the wrap in your thin fabric and two or more copies of the pad liner in your thick fabric – the more layers of the thick fabric you have, the more absorbent it will be. If you're adding a waterproof layer, cut it using the pad-liner pattern.

3 Sew the two copies of the wrap together with the sides that will eventually be on the outside facing each other.

4 Cut a small hole in the centre of just the top layer and use it to turn the fabric right side out – don't worry about this hole, it'll get covered in a moment so it won't fray.

5 Sew your layers of the thick fabric together to make the liner. Depending on the type of fabric, you could either use the inside-out technique like with the thin fabric, or you could just layer everything the right way round and sew the edges using a blanket stitch or overlock stitch to stop the edges from fraying. If you're adding a waterproof layer, put this on the bottom of the pile.

6 Sew the liner on to the top of the wrap, covering the hole.

7 Sew on your buttons or poppers to the wings – use your underwear as a guide so you know the best place to put them.

8 Now you have a reusable pad – admire your handiwork!

——————— **Pad liner**

——————— **Pad wrap**

Ways to customize

- Make it longer, shorter, wider or thinner.
- Experiment with different closure methods.
- Sew the liner inside the wrap instead of on top.
- Use a cute fabric with a fun pattern.

How to clean a reusable pad

It's really simple to clean reusable pads! After rinsing them to get most of the blood out, chuck them in the washing machine with your darks. Here's a few tips to make it easier:

- Rinse and wash in cold water, not hot. Warm water makes blood clot, so it will actually make your fabric more prone to staining. If you're using a washing machine, 30°C or 40°C is best.
- If the stain is really stubborn, soak the pad in cold water and soap for a day before washing it properly.
- Don't use fabric softener as it reduces the fabric's absorbency.
- Air dry rather than tumble dry. Tumble drying can shrink fabrics.
- Dry the pad in direct sunlight as UV light is a great bacteria killer.
- Add a few drops of essential oil, such as lavender or rose, to the water you're washing it in to keep it smelling nice.

Candice Chirwa (she/her)
Minister of Menstruation

I ovary-acted with my period stains . . .

Recently I was busy working at a restaurant and, feeling the need to go to the bathroom, I stood up, when a waitress kindly informed me that I had a stain down there. It finally happened. The Minister of Menstruation had stained her clothes. Yes, a period activist who is well-informed and empowered about period products, and uses a period app, stained her clothes. In that moment, my little imposter syndrome came crawling in, attempting to make me feel embarrassed and shy about this accident. But I just kept telling myself that there is nothing to be ashamed of – especially when it comes to menstrual blood.

So why can period stains feel so embarrassing in the first place?

I started my period when I was ten years old. I remember putting a lot of emphasis on hiding my period and making sure that no one saw if I stained my clothes. This instruction was further supported by the period horror stories presented in various pop-culture magazines, where readers shared how embarrassed they felt when 'Aunt Flo' made a splash on their favourite jeans.

So I knew I wasn't alone in feeling this way. In society, young people who menstruate are told that periods are dirty and gross. This kind of misinformation provides an element of shame and stigma that conditions us to hide our periods and most importantly not talk openly about them. I remember when I started, I wasn't told why they were disgusting, just that they were. I was told to make sure no one saw my period products and to wear dark clothing when I was on my period. No reason why, just do it. I wish in that moment I knew this: just like having body hair doesn't make you dirty, neither does having a period. If I had access to empowering, affirming and accurate education, I wouldn't have carried the shame and stigma for so long.

But just like me, if you do experience a period stain one day, there is no need to be embarrassed. The person who lets you know about it is just trying to help. If you were in their shoes, you'd do the same. If they are rude about it, don't pay them any attention. There's nothing wrong with you! Periods happen to more than 50% of the population, and the overflows and stains are a part of that.

Let's actively remove the stigma when it comes to speaking openly about periods. It starts with understanding what periods are, and what menstrual blood consists of. Once you have learnt that, you can start educating and spreading awareness to others. You could even campaign for society to provide free period products, because so many people would benefit from this.

We need to help each other through extending a little bit of kindness in whatever way possible.

ℭrowing a second body – I mean, a baby

Conception

Sometimes we're made to believe that the moment we have unprotected sex – BOOM! – we'll be pregnant. Turns out this isn't the case, as lots of things need to happen for a sperm and an egg to turn into a foetus.

Conception happens when a sperm cell fuses with an egg. It often happens in the ovarian tube, but it can happen in other places.[15] Conception is a pretty mind-blowing event, and how it happens is one of the great wonders of biology.

- The egg is the only cell in the human body big enough to be seen by the naked eye and is about 0.1 mm wide.

- Little hair-like structures called cilia push the egg down the ovarian tube towards the uterus and push sperm towards the egg.

- The egg is only able to be fertilized for 12–24 hours after ovulation.

- Sperm can remain alive inside the womb for up to five days.

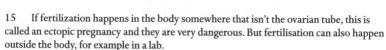

15   If fertilization happens in the body somewhere that isn't the ovarian tube, this is called an ectopic pregnancy and they are very dangerous. But fertilisation can also happen outside the body, for example in a lab.

- Sperm can detect or sniff out certain chemicals round the egg when they're nearby so they know where to go.

- Cervical mucus gets thinner when oestrogen levels are high around ovulation, making it easier for sperm to get through.

- The egg is surrounded by a thick layer that a sperm must penetrate. Many sperm cells must break through this layer for fertilization to happen, but only one will typically make it past the membrane and combine its DNA with the egg's.

Approximately 180 million sperm enter the vagina during ejaculation, but most never make it to the egg. They are killed off by:

- Acidic vaginal secretions.

- Getting stuck in the cervical mucus.

- Being destroyed by the immune system.

- Going down the wrong ovarian tube.

- Issues with the sperm itself, such as swimming problems or too many heads.

The first-ever mainstream pregnancy test involved a lot more than peeing on a stick. Between the 1940s and 1960s, doctors would inject a female African clawed frog with someone's urine, and if they were pregnant, the frog would lay eggs 5–12 hours later.

FERTILITY

The ability to conceive and give birth to a child is very dependent on the individual. Some people will have an easier time, and some a harder one. The idea that it's harder to conceive as you move from your 20s to your 30s to your 40s is massively overblown. A lot of the data presented to us on this is based on some really shaky science, with one of the most common stats based on a survey from 1670–1830 (yeah, a woman living in a world without antibiotics, refrigerators or central heating is a great baseline to use for people nowadays . . .) The things that affect your fertility in a much greater way are timing (the closer you are to ovulation, the higher your chances of becoming pregnant); certain health conditions, such as PCOS or endometriosis; your partner (it takes two to tango, and sometimes it's your partner who could have fertility issues); and environmental factors, such as being exposed to certain pollutants, based on your job or where you live.

When is the right time to have a baby?

While science can tell us averages and generalizations based off data, it's just not possible to be able to look at an individual and tell them when the best time is for them to have a baby from a biological point of view. There's just too many other factors involved. Instead, the decision must be based on personal priorities, such as:

- Emotional readiness

- Financial readiness

- Housing situation

- Other caring responsibilities

- Mental health

- Physical health

- Career goals

- Other life priorities

- The other partner (if you even want one!)

Fertility is such a sensitive issue, and it can be really difficult for people to talk about. It's always best to avoid asking someone if they're planning to have children unless they bring up the discussion first, because you never know what's going on in their lives.

More than one way

If you do get to a point when you want to have a child, there are lots of options when it comes to choosing how you bring them into your family. That's the beautiful thing about living in the 21st century: there's so many options available. And when the time is right, knowing what they are and making an informed choice is an empowering thing to do.

IVF

This stands for 'in vitro fertilization' and is when an egg and sperm are taken from two people's bodies and fertilized in a laboratory.

Egg freezing

This involves having some eggs removed from your ovaries and put 'on ice'. You might want to do this if you know your fertility might decline – for example, due to a health condition or gender-affirming surgery – or if you want a child but the timing isn't right. (The idea is that younger eggs may have a better chance at being fertilized than older ones.)

Surrogacy/gestational carrier

This is when a person carries a baby in their womb on behalf of another person. Traditional surrogacy is when the person carrying the baby also donates their egg, whereas a gestational carrier is someone who has an embryo made using other people's egg and sperm implanted in their uterus via IVF.

Egg/sperm donation

If you can't get pregnant with your own cells – perhaps because of infertility or being in a same-sex couple – you can use donated cells to make a baby.

Adoption

This is the act of legally bringing up a child as your own with different biological parents. Even though adoptive parents don't conceive the child themselves, this is a totally valid way to bring a child into your family.

Storks delivering babies

Still working on that method . . .

'I was told there would be glowing.'

The experience of pregnancy is different for everyone. From what we're shown on TV, you'd think it's just happy kicks in your tummy and a glowing complexion! However, it's not necessarily always sunshine and rainbows, and there's often so much we aren't told about being pregnant until it happens. Some people enjoy the experience, and others really don't (and that's totally OK!). The average pregnancy lasts for 40 weeks, and here's a very brief breakdown of the stages:

First trimester – conception to week 12

Usually, the first sign of pregnancy is missing a period. Other symptoms can include morning sickness, bigger breasts, peeing more and feeling tired – although some people don't experience any of this. The foetus starts off as a bunch of cells that soon develop into different organs. By week 12, the foetus is about the size of a lime.[16]

16 I don't know why foetuses are always compared to fruit, but I'm not sure how to buck the trend. Compare them to different sports balls? Or types of bread?

Second trimester – weeks 13 to 27

By the middle of this phase, a baby bump will probably start showing. Hopefully the morning sickness will have passed by now. Expectant parents can start feeling the foetus kick from around the 20th week. It's generally considered that a foetus can live outside the womb from around 24 weeks – before this, their organs aren't developed enough to survive on their own.

Third trimester – weeks 28 to 40

This stage is when the bump starts getting really big, and a bit uncomfortable. By the 36th week, the foetus will have likely moved to be facing head downward, preparing for birth.

Miscarriage and stillbirths

A miscarriage is losing a pregnancy during the first 23 weeks. A stillbirth is losing a baby beyond this point. Miscarriages are way more common than you might think – in fact, it's estimated that one in four pregnancies end in miscarriage. It's so common and yet rarely talked about.

Miscarriage can happen for so many reasons – genetic factors, a weak cervix, underlying health conditions, taking certain medications and that's just a few. What we do know is that there's loads of false information thrown around, and things such as exercising too much or having a fright do not cause miscarriages.

Losing a pregnancy is an extraordinarily emotional experience. It's normal to grieve. There are charities all over the world who can support people during such a difficult time. No one needs to suffer alone.

Your body, your choice

Every person should be able to decide what to do with their own body. That goes for having a baby, but also NOT having a baby. Roughly three out of ten pregnancies around the world end in an abortion and 95 per cent of people in the US don't regret having one. The decision must be yours and yours alone.

Abortions are incredibly safe. In the US, only 2 per cent have complications, while 16.4 per cent of pregnancies have complications. There are no long-term physical health effects of having one. And they do not affect your future fertility.

An abortion can be done in a hospital or clinic; with assistance over the phone with a medical professional; or at home with a prescription from a doctor. Do not go to a place called a 'crisis pregnancy centre'. This is a place where the people working there will try to manipulate you into not having an abortion, even if you want one – they are not to be trusted and you deserve better. A good doctor will inform you of all your options – not try to sway you one way or another, nor judge your choices. They will respect the decision you make.

The method used for an abortion depends on how far along the pregnancy is. There are two main types – a medical abortion or a surgical one. Medical abortions can take place either at home or in a hospital or clinic, and are performed by administering two different medications a couple of days apart. The embryo will then pass through the patient's vagina, usually a few hours after the second medication is taken. It looks and feels like a very heavy period with really bad cramps.

A surgical abortion can happen in a few ways. There is a vacuum aspiration where the pregnancy is removed using suction. It only takes about ten minutes and patients can usually go home the same day. The other kind is called a dilation and evacuation (D&E), during which forceps are used to remove the pregnancy. In extremely rare cases, an abortion can happen by inducing labour to pass the pregnancy – this usually happens if there are very severe health risks to continuing the pregnancy that weren't noticed until much further down the line.

I'm not going to lie to you – realizing you need to have an abortion can be extraordinarily emotional. It could be devastating, elating, scary or even a relief. All emotions – positive and negative – are valid. And it's OK to express these emotions – there is nothing to be ashamed of, whether you simply need a big hug or want to sing from the rooftops. Having an abortion is a big health decision, and making the right choice for you is one of the most powerful things you can do.

If you take misoprostol (a drug that causes abortions) in a place where abortion is illegal and you have complications, seek medical advice at a hospital or doctor's surgery and just tell them you are having a miscarriage. There's no blood test for misoprostol, so there's no way of them knowing unless you tell them. The treatment is the same regardless, so it's much better to get help than risk your life.

The big event: birth

Birth is a huge feat. It's the uterus's equivalent of running a marathon with parkour mixed in while hiking up Mount Everest. And on top of that, not everyone has access to the same standard of care – quality of care can be massively affected by factors such as wealth and class, race, gender and other axes of oppression.

There is no 'right' way to give birth. But just like pregnancy, as we often only tend to see it happen on television, we can have a skewed understanding of how it works. For example, did you know that your waters usually break during labour, not right at the start? Getting bad back pain or an urgent need to wee just doesn't make for quite as dramatic a TV moment though. There are two types of births: vaginal and Caesarean section.

Vaginal birth

In the past, people tended to give birth kneeling, squatting or sitting on a special chair. Nowadays, people often give birth lying on their back, as this helps the doctor see better. Research shows that giving birth on your back actually gives you a disadvantage – obviously, you want to work *with* gravity. As long as the birth is progressing normally, people can actually choose whichever position feels comfortable. Recovery takes time, but the myth about the vagina becoming looser afterwards is false – the tissue is elastic and vaginas don't stay baby-sized forever!

Caesarean section

A Caesarean section – or C-section for short – is an operation to deliver a baby via an incision in the belly. They can be planned or unplanned, and about one in four people who give birth in the UK do it via C-section. This can be due to a medical reason, such as the placenta being in a dangerous position, or a non-medical reason such as being able to control and plan the birth experience better (which is still totally valid!). It usually takes longer to recover from a C-section.

Birth is a huge deal. It literally involves moving a WHOLE HUMAN from your insides to your outsides! How could anyone deny the V is powerful after that?

Birth trauma

Birth can be a wonderful experience for some, ending with a super-cute baby. But it's important to know that giving birth isn't always a positive experience. Thirty thousand people a year in the UK experience a traumatic birth – whether that's due to complications or because of how the person giving birth was treated by the medical professionals, for instance when patients are not listened to or not being given enough information. Birth trauma usually happens to the person giving birth, but it can also affect their partners. Parents deserve autonomy and medical professionals must be taught to communicate effectively with their patients.

Mental health

Pregnancy and birth often puts a huge toll, not only on the body, but also the mind. It's really common to experience the 'baby blues' after giving birth, which is low mood for a week after delivery. There are also more serious conditions such as post-natal depression, postpartum psychosis, anxiety and eating disorders. These are all conditions for which there is support available.

A New Life Chapter

Here's a true fact for you: menopause lasts just one day. Doesn't sound so bad, does it?

(If you hadn't already guessed, that was a bit misleading, although *technically* it is true.)

Menopause is defined as the day when you've been 12 months without a period. The average age for menopause is 51. The bit leading up to menopause is called perimenopause, and postmenopause is everything after that one day of menopause.

Perimenopause shows up naturally around your forties, but it can be brought on earlier by a hysterectomy (surgical removal of the uterus), an oophorectomy (removal of the ovaries) or as a symptom of a health condition. During perimenopause, people start ovulating less frequently until eventually stopping altogether. Their ovaries slowly produce less oestrogen and progesterone but they don't stop making them completely, they just do so at a much lower level. Perimenopause can last a few years before periods stop completely. Symptoms can include irregular periods, vaginal dryness, pain during sex, changes in libido, hot flushes, headaches, mood swings, problems concentrating, palpitations and insomnia.

Why does it happen? Like, not how – whyyyyyy?

Humans are part of an exclusive club for going through the menopause. It's quite rare in nature and only a few other animals – such as pilot whales, orcas, beluga whales and narwhals – go through it. From an evolutionary point of view, it doesn't seem to make sense for fertility to end. There must be a good reason for the menopause, and scientists are trying to figure out what exactly it is.

My fave hypothesis is called The Grandmother Theory, and it basically says that grandmas are the reason humans are so great. The idea is that human babies are kind of useless – how can baby horses walk within hours of being born, but human babies take a whole year (or more) to learn? It's because our babies are essentially born prematurely. We have massive heads that store our massive brains, plus small hips to help us stand upright on two legs. That means that if we waited until a baby was fully cooked before giving birth, it would never be able to get out. A baby that can't walk or do anything except poo and cry needs loads of attention to make sure it stays alive. And who best to step in and show new parents the ropes? Someone who's already done it all – your own mum! But you don't want her distracted looking after her own babies, so menopause steps in to help her concentrate on making sure her grandkids make it to adulthood. What I'm saying is, give your grandma a call and say thank you. If it weren't for her, the human race would probably never have survived.

How to support someone going through the menopause

Some people LOVE the menopause – no more worrying about periods or unplanned pregnancies and no more hormonal mood swings. It's a whole new exciting chapter in life. On the other hand, some don't enjoy it at all. Not only can the symptoms of perimenopause be pretty bleurgh, but it can also feel like a loss of youth or a huge change in identity. Here's what you can do to show support to people going through the menopause:

- **Learn** – read up about the menopause to find out more.

- **Listen** – everyone's experience is different, so let them tell you what they are going through.

- **Be kind** – for many, menopause can be difficult, so focus on other things such as treating them kindly and doing favours.

- **Help** – symptoms can take a toll, so consider doing light exercise with them to alleviate symptoms or get them water if they have a hot flush.

Ways you can make a difference

This journey that our body goes on is shrouded in misinformation, mystery and shame. None of this does us any good – in fact, it makes life much more difficult. So I want to close this chapter with some suggestions for how to make things better for everyone and be a fanny-tastic V-activist:

- Talk openly about your period. No more euphemisms, such as 'painting the town red' or 'Aunt Flo's in town'.

- Call people out when they say bigoted things, such as complaining it must be someone's 'time of the month' if they're angry.

- Campaign to have your school or public buildings provide free menstrual products in all toilets (if they don't already).

- Ask your local representative to get rid of the tampon tax.

- Campaign for your country to create/fund free healthcare.

- Donate period products to your local food banks and shelters.

- Move to reusable period products (if that works for you).

- Go to the doctor if you have physical or mental health problems – don't leave it until it gets worse.

- Don't ask someone if/when they plan to have children unless they bring this up themselves.

- Don't touch people's pregnant bellies without their consent.

- Support reproductive justice charities.

- Be gender-inclusive with your language to acknowledge that it's not only women – nor all women – who menstruate, get pregnant and go through the menopause.

- Educate yourself by reading books, articles, listening to podcasts or watching documentaries about these topics.

Chapter 3
LET'S GET IT ON

It would be impossible to write a book about the wonders of the V without talking about sex. Part of embracing your V is to feel pleasure. In fact, it's one of my favourite things about having one! So, without further ado, let's get it on . . .

I'm going to start by asking you a question that might sound deceptively simple: **What is sex?**

Take a moment to think about what comes into your head. What body parts are going where? How many people are involved? What gender are the participants? Ask ten different people, and you'll get ten different answers. There's no definition everyone agrees on, which is actually GREAT NEWS. Because it means you get to decide your own definition. For you, sex could be:

- When a penis is inserted into a vagina.

- Using a hand or a mouth with a set of genitals.

- There could be no genitals involved at all.

- In person, on the phone, by video call (or even by letter if you want to be proper old-school!)

- With another person or by yourself.

As long as . . .

- you are over the age of consent, which in the UK is 16 (but it varies from country to country)

- and all participants are actively consenting

. . . then sex can be whatever you want it to be!

Sex is all around us, but society rarely shows the huge variety of what sex is. Often, it's a very narrow view centred around the penis, and this misses out the reality of the variety that sex has to offer.

Perhaps you have not had sex for the first time yet. Perhaps you've had loads and you're still perplexed. Perhaps you're an expert! Let's explore together the ins and outs of all things sex, consent and pleasure. If sex is something you want to do, it can be one of the most wonderful experiences this silly universe has to offer.

If you're a teenager reading this, you probably already know about things I didn't learn until I was, like, 25 – I didn't have the same access to the internet that you probably do nowadays. So, I'm not going to dumb anything down in this chapter, hide important information or be judgy. Instead, I'm going to devote this time to being **honest** about how sex works and what's involved. I also highly recommend following up on the resources mentioned in here and at the back of the book if you want to learn more.

You may have heard of the 'sex positivity movement'. It's centred on the idea that sex is a healthy part of life and all people deserve sexual pleasure in a safe and consensual way. It's in opposition to sex negativity, which says sex is wrong and immoral and people shouldn't like it (noooo, thank you). Though I totally agree with the philosophies underpinning the sex positivity movement, it's important to remember that people's relationship with sex can be very complicated. I'm much more interested in the idea of 'sex neutrality', which recognizes this complex relationship, understands that people often have other priorities than sex and removes the pressure that the word 'positivity' sometimes brings.

Muffbusting

Even before we start having sex, we are told quite a few things – from sex education at school, from friends and from the media – which are often false. It's so important to distinguish the myths from the truth in order to have great sex. I've gathered some of the most common sex myths and have taken the liberty to bust them for you with this handy fact file. (Don't worry if any of these ideas are news to you – we're going to be exploring most of them throughout the chapter.)

- Sex is NOT just putting a penis inside a vagina.

- Penetrative vaginal sex for the first time shouldn't be painful or make you bleed.

- Sex is about you as much as it's about your partner.

- There's no 'normal' age to have sex for the first time, as long as you are over the age of consent.

- Penetrative sex won't make your vagina looser.

- Sex won't make your labia bigger.

- Contraception is everyone's responsibility, not just the person with the V.

- STIs can happen to anyone, not just people with lots of partners.

- Bigger penises aren't always better. What's more important is how you use your body and mind.

- The goal of sex doesn't have to be having an orgasm.

- Sex isn't great every time and that's OK.

- Sex in real life is rarely like what you see in porn.

- Masturbation isn't harmful – in fact, it has loads of benefits.

- Just because you have a partner doesn't mean you have to stop masturbating.

- Getting older doesn't mean the end of sex.

The truth about virginity

When someone has sex for the first time, we tend to call this 'losing your virginity'. Before I go on to explain the problem with this concept, there's some things I would like to say about your first time:

1 Don't let anyone pressure you into having sex for the first time if you don't feel ready or simply don't want to do it.

2 Equally, don't let anyone stop you from having sex if you do want to.

3 When you do have sex for the first time, this changes **absolutely nothing** about your worth or personhood. You are valuable **no matter** your sexual history.

4 There's no way of knowing if someone has had sex for the first time, despite what some believe. We've already talked about the myths of the hymen, but the lie that it will break, bleed and cause pain when a penis first enters a vagina is not only wildly false – it's also enough to make anyone with a vagina believe that sex is unpleasant and not about pleasure at all (some might say that's the point of the myth!). This is **absolutely not the case**. Sex **should be** pleasurable.

5 Usually we think of 'losing your virginity' as when a penis goes into a vagina for the first time. But this is not the only way to have sex, and it ignores the lived experiences of queer people. **All types of sex are equally valid and important.**

If there is only one thing you take away from this book, let it be this: virginity is a social construct. What does this mean? It means that literally nothing biological changes when you have sex for the first time. Nothing pops; you don't start glowing; you don't get some stamp on you that says 'THIS PERSON HAS NOW EXPERIENCED SEX!!!'. The concept of virginity has been created by human society and has no basis in biology.

The concept of virginity was invented thousands of years ago as a way of enforcing the kyriarchy. The theory goes that when DNA tests weren't available, men wanted reassurance that any babies their wives gave birth to were definitely theirs in order to prevent them potentially giving their wealth to somebody else's kid. Basically, it's capitalism ruining everything. How did they achieve this? By coming up with ways to pressure women into only having sex with one man, and remaining 'virgins' until marriage. Having a baby out of wedlock has long been stigmatized, and families didn't want to be shamed by their communities, so they enforced this system. We still see these outdated views in society today in the form of slut-shaming.

The term 'losing' is also problematic. When you lose something, you are less whole. It's something you need to hold on to in order to be valuable. This is not true! You are no less important or special once you start having sex, and I need you to remember that!

Virginity and the idea of losing it was invented to put us in our place. We say: **no longer**. No more shaming based on outdated stigmas. Your worth is not tied to your sexual history. Once you are over the age of consent, it is up to you and you alone when you have sex with someone else for the first time, and any decision you make that works for you is the right one.

Consent – what is it?

Consent should be the foundation of all sex. You might have heard people describing it as 'sexy', but do you know what? It's more than that. It's **necessary**. Asking for consent can feel awkward, but you have to push through. What's more awkward – asking a question that makes you feel weird or violating someone's boundaries? The latter, obvs. Consent should be two things:

1 Enthusiastic

Your partner needs to be an active and enthusiastic participant. You can discuss how your partner is feeling, exactly what they want to do and their boundaries. You can tell if someone is enthusiastic by looking at their body language, their facial expression or the words they are using. Consent isn't just the absence of a no – it's a 'hell yeah'.

2 Specific

Check in regularly, and with each new thing you want to do. You or your partner can change their mind mid-act and that's OK. You also need to disclose any relevant and important information, such as any STIs you might have or when your last STI test was.

Consent only counts if a person has freedom and capacity to consent. That means even if they say yes, if they are under the age of consent, drunk, asleep or being forced or bullied, a 'yes' doesn't count and sex should not be happening.

A 'no' must always be respected. Bear in mind that no isn't always just saying 'no' – it's also body language, making an excuse, postponing, changing the subject or negotiation.

HOW TO TALK ABOUT CONSENT

ASK FOR IT

- I'm feeling sexy. Shall we . . .?
- Would you like it if we . . .?
- Do you want it fast/slower?
- I'd really like to do this thing. Would you be into that?

GIVE IT

- Hell, yes!
- That sounds hot.
- That feels good.
- *wiggle your eyebrows in a suggestive but hilarious and charming fashion*
- I've never done that but would like to try. Can we start off slow?

CHECK IN

- Can we pause?
- It's OK if you're not into this.
- Would you like to try something else?
- Was that your left or my left?
- Would you like to stop?

REFUSE OR WITHDRAW IT

- No.
- I appreciate the offer, but no, thanks.
- I can't, I need to get back home.
- I'm not into that.
- I said no, and you're not changing my mind so drop it.
- Please stop. You're making me feel uncomfortable.
- *physically push their hand away*

When consent gets grey

You may have heard the phrase 'yes means yes and no means no'. But the reality can be a lot more complicated than this. Sometimes we say yes when we want to say no. It might be because we are afraid the person propositioning us will become judgemental or even violent if we say no or for many other reasons. Being able to say no is – unfortunately – a privilege, and consent is a lot greyer than we might expect.

I so desperately wish, dear reader, that I could reach out from this page and give you a great big hug and tell you everything in life will be OK. I wish I could be a big sister to every single one of you and protect you always. I wish I could say that everyone will respect your boundaries because it's the right thing to do. But sometimes life doesn't happen that way.

Sometimes the problem is that the other person doesn't recognize the importance of consent or understand the signals you're giving. However, other times it might be that the person just doesn't care. This is part of a much wider societal problem – the kyriarchy. Our mission should be to dismantle it so we can live in a world where everyone respects people's boundaries, understands what consent is and the damage that can be caused by not respecting it. I hope you will join me on this mission.

However, unfortunately the world isn't there yet. Finding yourself in a difficult situation where your consent has been violated is never your fault. And I don't want you to think that me giving you tips on how to get out of situations like this is me victim-blaming you. It's only an acknowledgement that life doesn't always go according to plan and I want you to have the skills and knowledge to look after yourself. There are times when sex has happened in this scary grey area of consent for me, and as I've grown up, I've realized it's something that happens to a lot of people, especially women.

If you find yourself in a situation where you were assaulted or felt like you had to say yes when you wanted to say no, here are some tips on what to do. This advice has been adapted from Planned Parenthood, a US-based non-profit organization that provides sexual health care:

- Remember, it's not your fault. It's **never** your fault.

- Get to a safe place as soon as possible.

- If you are in immediate danger, call the emergency services (if you can).

- If you are under the age of consent, tell a trustworthy adult immediately.

- Seek medical care. You may need physical medical care, such as emergency contraception, testing for STIs, PEP (a preventative medicine for HIV) and you may also need mental medical care such as the services of a counsellor or therapist.

- If you're going to the police, don't wash – they'll need to take samples from your body to use as evidence. If you want to change your clothes, keep hold of them so they can be tested.

- Lean on your support network. No person is an island and there is no shame in needing the help of a loved one.

- Seek out resources such as a rape crisis centre or support line. You can find examples of these at the back of the book.

Some Sexy FAQs

The scene is set. You've got two consenting adults. You're ready to go. Ummm . . . now what?

Should we do foreplay?

If you're planning to have sex, foreplay is the stuff you do before genitals get involved. It can include anything from kissing and sexy talk to exploring each other's bodies with your hands or mouth. The decision on how much foreplay you do is personal preference, but the whole point of foreplay is to build excitement and have some fun. My advice? YES! Do it! And enjoy it! Honestly, foreplay is just as good (and for some even better) than doing anything genital-based. Also, it will make you more aroused and make genital-stuff feel even better.

Do I need lube?

Trust me on this: lube is your best friend. Wetter is better! The wetter you are, the more comfortable penetrative sex is, and it reduces friction in general. Not everyone makes enough natural lubrication when they are aroused – this can be for loads of reasons, and there's absolutely no shame in using lube to enhance the experience. If lube helps you have better sex, go for it!

However, if you aren't wet enough because you are feeling uncomfortable or unsafe, or you haven't done enough foreplay, then using lube isn't going to help a lot and your best bet is to address those issues first.

If you're using a condom, the extra moisture from the lube reduces the chances of it breaking. There's loads of different kinds of lube: silicone-based, water-based, hybrid (silicone and water), oil-based and pure oil. Do not use oil-based lube and latex condoms! It will break down the latex, making the condom less effective. And be careful when using silicone-based lube, as it can damage certain contraceptive methods made from silicone and silicone sex toys.

What is an orgasm?

An orgasm is the sudden involuntary release of sexual tension. Orgasms can happen because of genital stimulation, breast stimulation or even in your dreams with no physical stimulation at all! It's a bit hard to describe what they feel like as they come in all sorts of flavours. They can be really strong, as though a wave is crashing across your whole body or they can be really weak, like a little ping between your legs. Often orgasms come with muscle contractions of the pelvic floor, but they can happen without these contractions too. And while some people may feel 'done' or 'complete' after an orgasm, some people don't get this feeling at all. There's actually no guarantee that an orgasm can leave you feeling one way or another, as it's so personal to the individual.

For most people with vulvas, the most reliable way to reach orgasm is by stimulating the clitoris. The glans clitoris is extremely sensitive, and for many it can even be painful to touch directly, particularly if they aren't aroused enough. If this is the case, it helps to touch it through the clitoral hood or through a piece of fabric, such as your underwear.

You might have heard about different types of orgasms – a 'vaginal' orgasm, 'clitoral' orgasm, 'G-spot' orgasm. Historically, there's been this idea that the 'correct' or best way to have an orgasm is through vaginal penetration.[17] If you don't orgasm solely from vaginal penetration, you're totally normal and actually in the majority. Ultimately, orgasms are orgasms. **There's no right or wrong way to have one**. The only thing that matters is if you enjoyed it.

17 Blame Sigmund Freud.

And the good news is that you can still have great sex even without having an orgasm.[18] They do not need to be the goal of sex – the best thing to do is just be present and enjoy the moment.

> **Some people cry after an orgasm. Orgasms are a release of tension, and I don't know if our brains can really differentiate between different types of tension, so sometimes tears just come out. Totally normal.**

What is 'squirting'?

Often called 'female ejaculation', this is the sudden release of fluid from the vulva during sex. There have been very few studies into what causes squirting. The most likely answer is that it's fluid produced by the lesser vestibular glands. But it could also be contractions of the pelvic floor forcefully emptying the bladder. Or it could be a combination of both. While for some people the fluid may seem like pee, for others it's a totally different fluid. For some, it's a regular occurrence, and for others, it rarely or never happens. **All of this is normal**.

Squirting is definitely real, but in many porn videos, it's common for performers to either fill up their vagina with water just before filming the 'squirting shot' or to just be urinating. So don't believe everything you see online.

---

18 Anorgasmia is when you don't experience orgasms. It's surpirsingly common, but it is something you can talk to your doctor about if you're concerned.

What is queefing?

During vaginal penetration, air can get caught up in there from all the pumping. When the air escapes and makes a loud *prrrrp*, this is a queef! It's not a fart, and it doesn't smell. It just makes a similar sound, because, physics. It is a completely natural bodily function, and there's no reason to be insecure or embarrassed about it.

What about sex toys?

Sex toys come in all shapes, sizes, colours and with all features – you name it, and it probably exists. Lots of people use sex toys. For some, it's the only way they can orgasm; for others, it's an exciting extra to the sexual experience. They are fantastic, and honestly vibrators are one of the top things that make me glad I was born in the 20th century. You know, along with central heating and antibiotics or whatever. But mostly vibrators. Here are my top tips: always wash the toy after use, look for 'discreet packaging' if you're doing online delivery and never use a broken toy. Seriously, it's not worth electrocuting your vagina. Also, the toy should be made of medical-grade or body-safe silicone, stainless steel or thermoplastic rubber – it's important that they are high quality.

Have you heard the rumour that vibrators were invented because doctors used to masturbate their patients in Victorian times and needed an alternative because they were getting cramp in their hand? TOTAL LIE. Doctors did not do this. The first vibrator was invented by Joseph Mortimer

Granville in the 1880s, and it was created to relieve muscle pains. But he specifically never tested it on women! People then realized it could be used on other parts of the body, and soon after people started using vibrators on their genitals. As soon as some new technology is invented, humans will find a way to use it for sex!

What happens after sex?

The moments after sex are often an overlooked part of the experience but are just as important as the main event.

Aftercare

Aftercare is the time after sex when you and your partner check in and take care of each other. Sex puts you in an emotional and vulnerable position, and this feeling becomes very apparent once sex is finished. Aftercare can take the form of talking about what happened and what you liked or didn't like, eating, drinking, cuddling, kissing, doing an activity together, giving a massage or doing something nice for your partner.

Clean up

You may want to wash your vulva – a rinse with warm water should do the trick. If you have used a toy, clean it promptly following the instructions on the packaging.

Check the condom and bin it

If you were using a condom, remove it, tie up the end so it doesn't leak and check for rips. If it did rip (which is unlikely if you use them properly, but it's always a possibility), get some emergency contraception and an STI test.

Content warning: sexual assault

You may have heard of something called 'stealthing', which is when a condom is secretly removed during sex without both partners' consent. It is a form of rape. If it happens to you, follow the advice earlier in the chapter. If you think your partner might do it, first communicate with them how important consent is and make sure they are on the same page as you. Visually check the condom is still in place during sex and do it with the lights on to make that easier. But if there's ever doubt, you can always say no! Find a partner who will respect you instead.

Getting the party started

Sex isn't a drive – it's like driving

In the 1990s, Dr John Bancroft and Dr Erick Janssen at the Kinsey Institute created a new theory called the 'dual control model of sexual response' to explain how we experience desire. They argue that there isn't a 'sex drive' that's pushing your body to want sex, but rather there are things that you get turned on by **and** things you get turned off by. They are usually likened to the accelerator and a brake on a car. In fancy science terms they are called the 'sexual excitation system' and the 'sexual inhibition system'.

The two systems work together, and getting sexually aroused requires two things to happen: the accelerator to be activated and the brake to be deactivated. It's all about trying to find a balance that works for you. Every person is different, and something that pumps the brakes for one person may in fact hit the accelerator for another!

Here are some examples of things that might activate your accelerator and brake.

HITTING THE GAS – THE SEXUAL EXCITATION SYSTEM	PUMPING THE BRAKES – THE SEXUAL INHIBITION SYSTEM
• Your partner is super hot and you're enjoying looking at them.	• Worrying what the other person will think about you.
• Your partner gives you a compliment.	• Worrying if your partner is enjoying themselves.
• Having a sexy fantasy.	• Feeling like there are high expectations for how to act or feel.
• Your partner is doing something really nice for you.	• Your partner doesn't seem very interested in you or doesn't respect you.
• Feeling good about the way you look.	• Life is super stressful or you're in a bad mood.
• Your partner is touching or kissing you.	• Feeling unsafe or pressured into doing something.
• An amazing smell.	• You've had bad experiences in the past that have made you fearful.
• Eye contact.	• Your partner has been really annoying you recently.
• Watching your partner get super excited talking about something they're passionate about.	• Worrying whether you'll be able to orgasm.
• Needing to de-stress.	• Your partner came on too strong or too fast.
• Talking about sexy things.	• Having an unmet need that's distracting you, for example being hungry or cold.
• You've done something to get adrenaline pumping.	
• A bad smell or an annoying noise.	

Context is so important to sexual desire – something might turn you on one day but turn you off another. Desire won't come as readily if you're stressed because stress is your brain trying to protect you from threats. But if you're feeling safe and calm, you're more likely to find more things sexy because your brain feels protected and you will feel more curious and open.

Sensitivity

These two systems can vary in sensitivity between different people. Having a sensitive accelerator means you get turned-on very easily, while having a less sensitive accelerator means you need to concentrate quite hard to get aroused. A sensitive brake means you get turned-off very easily, and a less sensitive one means you may find yourself getting aroused in inappropriate situations. Where your sensitivity falls on these two systems is super personal and makes you unique – that's why there's no 'one size fits all' approach to getting the party started.

And you can use this knowledge to help you! You wouldn't drive a car if you didn't know how the pedals worked, so to be able to take control over your sexual experiences, you need to know how **your** pedals work! Prioritizing your own pleasure is a very empowering thing to do. So learn what turns you on, identify what turns you off, and hopefully this will help you feel confident, relax and enjoy the moment!

What's the difference between feeling horny and a wet vagina? (Not a trick question)

Often when you're aroused, your body responds physically. However, sometimes what you're feeling and how your body reacts don't match up. This is called 'arousal non-concordance'. It's super normal and extremely common – it happens to everyone. It's because our genitals generally respond to anything sex-related, but it's our brain that decides whether we like it or not – and sometimes they don't work in tandem. What this means is that it's totally normal if you're really excited to have sex with someone but don't have a physical response (such as a wet vagina or a hard clitoris) or to have this physical response even when you aren't feeling turned-on or excited. When you tell partners about this, they will often respond by asking, 'But if I can't tell how aroused you are by how wet your vulva is, how can I tell???' And here is the answer: 'By the words coming out of my mouth.'

How a vulva responds is the same as a penis. It's thought that penises get hard and vulvas get wet, but actually both do both. People with penises get pre-cum and people with vulvas get a hard clitoris!

What comes first in desire?

There are two ways desire can happen: spontaneous and responsive. Spontaneous desire happens in **anticipation** of sexual pleasure (like glimpsing your partner when they're looking really sexy and your body going 'give me summa that!'). Responsive desire happens in **response** to sexual pleasure (like getting a soft kiss on the neck and your body going 'more of that, please and thank you'). Most people experience both kinds of desire, but often people lean more towards one type than the other. Neither is better or worse than the other – both are totally valid.

A cum-clusion

So what does all this knowledge mean? It means everyone experiences desire and pleasure in different ways. THAT IS TOTALLY NORMAL. Knowing how your body works means you can work with it instead of trying to force it to do something against its nature. For example, if life is starting to feel stressful and you find you aren't getting very turned-on – this is TOTALLY NORMAL.[19] There's nothing wrong with you – you just need to address the stress and move to a better context (easier said than done, I know). Don't fight against your body – work with it. This is the true key to a fulfilling sex life.

19 Sometimes people want more sex in response to stress and that's also totally normal.

You've probably heard it said that biologically, men have high sex drives and women have low sex drives. FALSE! In fact, the female orgasm was generally considered exceptionally important in the West for centuries as it was believed that conception only happened if both people orgasmed. There have been lots of cultures in the past that welcomed female sexuality (which you'll read more about in chapter 5). In medieval Europe, they believed women had the high sex drives and men the low ones. Much of this narrative changed around the 1800s. The field of sexology was established and society's attitudes towards female sexuality shifted. Husbands were no longer encouraged to stimulate their wife's clitoris if they wanted children (a truly sad day). Freud said that clitoral orgasms were a sign of 'immaturity'. Women were discouraged from using bicycles when they were first invented because the vibrations of the seat were considered damaging to the organs. Race science made false claims that Black and Indigenous women were more sexual by saying they had larger labia and clitorises (of course, all completely not true) as a way to enforce white supremacy. Much of our modern experience and understanding of sexual oppression doesn't come from biology – it's been socially constructed over the last few hundred years.

HOW TO HAVE GREAT SEX

- Communication, communication, communication! No one is a mind reader (if only!). If you want something to happen or to stop, you need to tell your partner.

- Learn what activates your accelerator and brakes, and how sensitive they are. Learn your partner's too!

- Actively create a good context by paying attention to your state of mind and environment.

- Practise mindfulness in the bedroom – put away thoughts about the past or future and just focus on right here, right now.

- Trust. Great sex can only happen when you trust the person you're with. That doesn't mean you have to know them inside out – it just means feeling comfortable being open with them and confident they'll listen to and respect you.

- Empathy – which goes both ways. Tune in to your partner and how they are feeling and let it guide you.

- Don't 'yuck someone's yum'. If someone expresses interest in something you don't like, don't shame them.

- Remember that everyone is unique and what some people like may not be what other people like.

- Don't be afraid to laugh. Sometimes funny things happen in bed! Being silly and light-hearted will lessen inhibitions and make communication easier.

- Stop worrying about what the internet, social media, magazines, friends or society in general tell you about sex. Leave judgement at the door and focus on what feels good for you.

- Practise self-compassion. There is no benefit to judging yourself when sex isn't good – you can only let yourself feel what you feel and allow it to move on. If you have a negative thought, acknowledge it, then gently let it go and return yourself to kindness.

- Be patient. Sometimes sex isn't good (particularly the first time with someone new). The more you do it, the more you'll realize what you and your partner like and dislike, and the better the sex will become.

- Slow down – the longer you allow yourself and the more gradually you build up to the moment, the better, and often more intense, the experience will be (most of the time).

- Try not to be too goal-orientated. Having an orgasm is just one part of sex, and it's not necessary to having a good time. Trying too hard to orgasm or to make your partner orgasm can put pressure on the experience, which is a big brake activator. Focus on the journey, not the destination.

- Always remember the four Cs – consent, communication, care and caution.

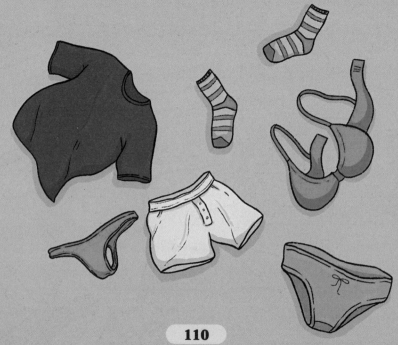

Where to learn more

There are so so so many resources to learn about sex. I am delighted that we now live in a world where feminism is back on the rise and it has brought with it so many wonderful resources about feminist sex – from TV shows to movies, to books to websites. When I was a teenager, my only resource for learning about sex was from *Cosmo*[20] and the website Scarleteen.com (which is still great, btw).

Here are my recommendations for some good places to start if you'd like more positive sex ed in your life, especially if you are interested in some things not covered by the scope of this book.

- **S.E.X.** by Heather Corinna (book)

- **Sex Ed: A Guide for Adults** by Ruby Rare (book)

- **Come As You Are** by Dr Emily Nagoski (book)

- **Sexpression:UK** (Young persons' charity)

- **Brook** (Sexual health service for young people)

- **BISH** (Online guide to sex for people aged 14+)

20 I can't tell you how happy I am that the days of recommending putting a doughnut on his dick are (almost) over.

Eliza Rainbow (they/them)
Content creator

Disability and sex

I'm Eliza. I'm a nonbinary content creator from London. I'm Disabled . . . AND I have sex!

When we talk about Disabled people, we often see them as 'non-sexual beings'. Disabled people are regularly excluded when we talk about sex education, and when we discuss Disabled people having sex, people seem to automatically look uncomfortable!

But here's the key thing: as long as all parties are able to enthusiastically consent, then yes! Disabled people have sex!

A little about me . . . I have rainbow hair, I live with my dog, Pod, and my partner, Michael, and finally, I'm a wheelchair user! That last one is almost definitely the least interesting part about me, although to many non-disabled people it automatically becomes the MOST interesting . . .

'What happened to you then?' 'Does anything work down there?' 'Wow, your partner stayed!'

Delightful. *Eye roll*

The truth is yes, my partner 'stayed' because I am a fabulous partner! Being a wheelchair user does not change that at all! Just as being a Disabled person doesn't change the fact that for me personally, I love to have sex.

Now, I am just one Disabled person and everyone is different – but for me sex is important. It means connection, fun, laughs and of course, it feels good too!

Sex may look a little bit 'different' for a Disabled person. I can't get into some positions; I may need to use different sex aids and I might not be able to have sex as 'much as other people' (not that there's a standard number of times that people do it!). However, that doesn't make my sex any less valid or important.

For me, sex is about connection and this can be felt in other ways too. My health fluctuates day to day, and if I am not feeling well enough for sex, then a hug or massage instead may feel just as good. These are just as valid and important as having sex!

Disabled people are natural adaptors.

Roll up somewhere and only see stairs? OK, let's find another way around! Not being given the support I need at school? OK, time to make sure this changes!

We have to adapt every single day because the world certainly does not adapt for us. I can't even leave my house without nearly being thrown out of my chair due to unsafe pavements. But this skill of adaptation is great in the bedroom!

Can't do a certain position? OK, let's adapt it! Pain in your hand making you struggle to get the right spot? Here's a sex toy for that! We have literally spent our entire lives adapting and the bedroom is no different.

As I said before, I am just one Disabled person and this is just my experience. That's the thing about the community – it's very diverse, and to get the best understanding about disability it's important to talk and learn from lots of different Disabled people.

What to take away from my short piece? Yes, Disabled people have sex. No, our partners are not heroes for staying with us. And yes, we know how to adapt!

I hope this has opened your eyes a little to the world of disability and sex. But these are just the basics

and there is much, much more to learn!

SOLO SEX IS NOT ONLY OK, IT'S GREAT

Solo sex, or masturbation, is a wonderful thing.[21] There's no 'right way' to do it – as long as you're in private and not hurting yourself, then do whatever feels good. Not everyone does it, and that's totally OK, but if the world of solo sex is new to you, here are some of the reasons why it's amazing:

- Orgasms make you feel good.

- Touching yourself will help you understand what feels good without the pressure of someone else's needs getting in the way.

- It helps you fall asleep.

- By taking time to focus on your needs, masturbation is self-care.

- It can ease pain – especially period pain.

- It's great for de-stressing.

- Sexual pleasure is a human right, and this is one way to guarantee it.

- You'll be giving the patriarchy a big 'fuck you'.

TOP TIPS

Make sure you're either alone in the house or the door is locked!

- Use lube! It's not just for partnered sex.

- Try out different sensations, movements and positions to figure out what you like. Don't be afraid to try new things! Solo sex is a great, low-pressure situation to explore your feelings without having to worry about someone else's pleasure.

21 Having both grown up in religious backgrounds, my ex liked to make a joke that if God didn't want us to masturbate, our arms wouldn't have been made that long.

- Say no to shame – solo sex is nothing to be guilty about.
- Just because you're in a relationship doesn't mean you have to stop.

Looking behind the porn curtain

Reminder: pornography is for people over 18.

Whether we like it or not, porn is part of the modern world. It's not going anywhere, so we've got to understand what it really is and how to navigate it ethically.

Sex educator Ruby Rare divides porn into three different types:

1 Mainstream – traditional porn (the one you're probably imagining when you think of porn).

2 Ethical – less about what you see on screen and more about what happens off screen.

3 Amateur – made by everyday people rather than professionals. (Often it's uploaded to a mainstream website and it's hard to verify if all people involved are legal and consenting so be very careful.)

It's important to know that mainstream porn is rarely realistic. This type of porn is to sex like *Fast and Furious* is to taking a drive down a motorway. It is not representative of real sex or the population at large, and it rarely shows contraception use or active consent or the important prep work that goes into making your body ready for certain types of sex. It can also often be problematic and fetishize[22] various identities in a way that is racist, misogynistic, ableist and/or transphobic. It showcases a very restricted range of bodies and genitals, and the vulvas in mainstream porn are usually completely shaved and have tiny labia.

Hallmarks of ethical porn include: everyone getting paid fairly, a safe working environment, a consent policy, content that shows real sexual pleasure and a variety of body types. It's usually provided online for a fee (although it's not uncommon for it to be stolen and uploaded on a free mainstream porn website).

Porn can be visual, such as videos or photos, or it can be drawn, animated, audio or text. The great thing about text, drawn or animated porn is that you know for a fact that none of the performers are being exploited because they are fictional!

---

22 Fetishization is when something is made into a sexual fetish. When that's feet or something, that's totally fine. But when it's an identity – like a race – that is dehumanizing.

A smorgasbord of contraception

CATEGORY	TYPE
Barrier methods that can protect you against STIs (these are the **only** kind of contraception that can prevent STIs) If you don't know whether your partner has an STI, you need to use a barrier method any time genitals come into contact with another set of genitals, an anus, a face, a mouth or a hand. STIs can infect places that aren't just your genitals.	Internal condom
	External condom
	Dental dam
Barrier methods that can't protect you against STIs These methods need to be left in place for at least 6 hours after sex. They are more effective if you use them with spermicide, which is a cream or gel that stops sperm from swimming. However, this can throw off the community of good bacteria that live in your vagina and some people are allergic to it.	Diaphragm
	Cervical cap
	Birth control sponge
Long-acting reversible contraception These are tiny devices that must be inserted by a medical professional. The benefit is that you don't need to remember to use them or interrupt sex for them to work	Hormonal IUD
	Copper IUD

If you want to have sex and you'd like to avoid having a baby or getting an STI, there's really only one thing to do – use contraception. There are so many options available to us, so I'm going to take you on a whistle-stop tour of some of the most common methods. I'd also recommend the website bedsider.org, which has even more detailed info.

WHAT ARE THEY AND HOW DO THEY WORK?	HOW ARE THEY USED AND WHY ARE THEY USEFUL?
A sheath that goes in the vagina or anus that blocks sperm.	Internal condoms can be super useful because you can put these on before sex, which is great if you don't like pausing the action. They are sometimes called 'female condoms'.
A sheath that goes on a penis to block sperm and block STI transmission.	External condoms can be put on just before penetration. Sometimes called 'male condoms'.
A square piece of latex that provides a barrier between mouths and vulvas or anuses.	These can be put on before starting oral sex. You can make your own dental dam by cutting up a condom. A link for instructions to make your own dental dam is in the further resources section on page 279.
A little cap that covers your cervix so no sperm can get past	Can be put in up to 2 hours before sex.
Similar to a diaphragm but smaller.	Can be put in up to 3 hours before sex.
A round piece of plastic foam that contains spermicide and blocks the cervix. The string is so you can remove it easily.	Can be put in up to 24 hours before sex.
A device that goes in the womb and releases the hormone progestin, which thickens your cervical mucus and prevents sperm getting past.	IUDs can work for 3 to 10 years before they need replacing, depending on the brand.
A copper device that goes in the womb. Copper is like kryptonite for sperm and makes it difficult for them to swim.	

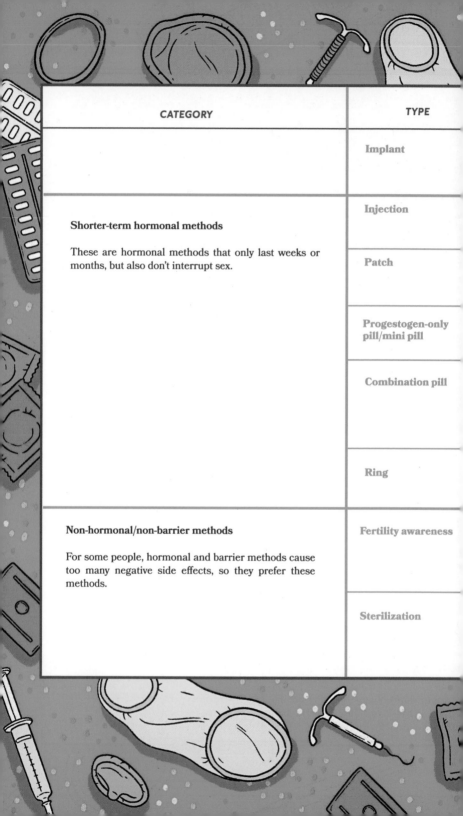

CATEGORY	TYPE
	Implant
Shorter-term hormonal methods These are hormonal methods that only last weeks or months, but also don't interrupt sex.	Injection
	Patch
	Progestogen-only pill/mini pill
	Combination pill
	Ring
Non-hormonal/non-barrier methods For some people, hormonal and barrier methods cause too many negative side effects, so they prefer these methods.	Fertility awareness
	Sterilization

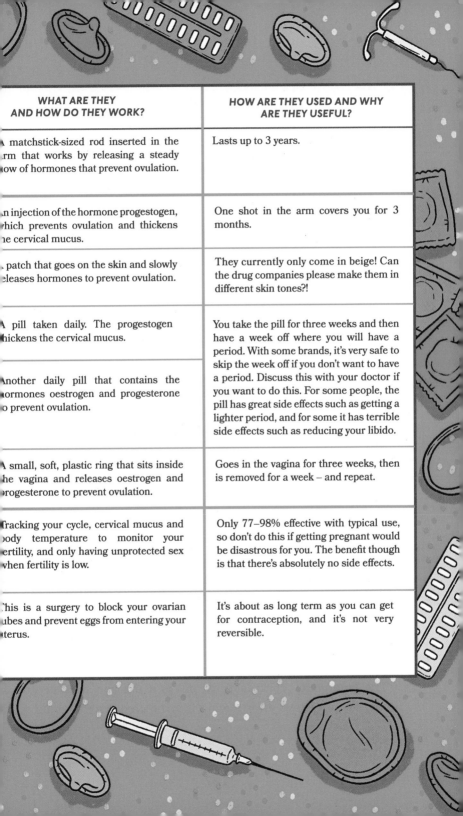

WHAT ARE THEY AND HOW DO THEY WORK?	HOW ARE THEY USED AND WHY ARE THEY USEFUL?
A matchstick-sized rod inserted in the arm that works by releasing a steady flow of hormones that prevent ovulation.	Lasts up to 3 years.
An injection of the hormone progestogen, which prevents ovulation and thickens the cervical mucus.	One shot in the arm covers you for 3 months.
A patch that goes on the skin and slowly releases hormones to prevent ovulation.	They currently only come in beige! Can the drug companies please make them in different skin tones?!
A pill taken daily. The progestogen thickens the cervical mucus.	You take the pill for three weeks and then have a week off where you will have a period. With some brands, it's very safe to skip the week off if you don't want to have a period. Discuss this with your doctor if you want to do this. For some people, the pill has great side effects such as getting a lighter period, and for some it has terrible side effects such as reducing your libido.
Another daily pill that contains the hormones oestrogen and progesterone to prevent ovulation.	
A small, soft, plastic ring that sits inside the vagina and releases oestrogen and progesterone to prevent ovulation.	Goes in the vagina for three weeks, then is removed for a week – and repeat.
Tracking your cycle, cervical mucus and body temperature to monitor your fertility, and only having unprotected sex when fertility is low.	Only 77–98% effective with typical use, so don't do this if getting pregnant would be disastrous for you. The benefit though is that there's absolutely no side effects.
This is a surgery to block your ovarian tubes and prevent eggs from entering your uterus.	It's about as long term as you can get for contraception, and it's not very reversible.

Top tips[23] for using condoms!

- Don't double up condoms (i.e. don't use one on top of the other or both external and internal). The friction makes them more likely to break.

- Use the correct size as using a larger size than needed will actually make it less likely to be effective.

- Always change the condom between sexual activities – for example, when switching from oral to vaginal sex.

- Don't open the packages with your teeth! You risk breaking the condoms and that's super unsexy.

Sometimes, you can forget to use contraception (but please do try to remember!) or your main method fails. Don't worry though, as there are three main back-up methods available:

- IUDs can be used as emergency contraception, and then they can be your primary method for years after. They must be inserted no later than five days after having unprotected sex.

- The emergency contraceptive pill is a pill you take up to three or five days after having unprotected sex (depending

23 Haha – 'tip'

on the brand). It is very important to understand that these pills don't end pregnancies – they only prevent them from happening, and the sooner you take them, the more likely they are to work. The standard dosage is only effective if you weigh up to 70 kg. If you weigh more than this, discuss it with your pharmacist or doctor to ensure the correct dosage.

- If you do get pregnant but don't want to be, abortions are available (depending on which country you're in). It's covered in the previous chapter if you'd like a refresher.

What are your priorities when choosing a contraceptive?

Just like so much when talking about the V, what's right for you can depend on so many things. Here are some things to consider, but if you have other priorities, that's totally fine too – remember: you do YOU.

- How effective is it at preventing pregnancy?
- How good is it at STI prevention?
- What are the side effects?
- Do you have any health conditions that need to be considered?
- Are you concerned about interrupting the flow of sex?
- Do you mind taking hormones?
- Will you need a safe place to store it, and do you have one?
- Are you forgetful and need something mistake-proof?
- How often do you need to use it or get it replaced?
- How much does it cost?
- Does it require a lot of effort to use?

- How easy is it to get?

- Will it help in other ways, such as with acne or period cramps?

- What will it do to your periods?

- If you decide to try for a baby, how quickly can you regain fertility?

- How much self-control does it require?

- Can you use it while breastfeeding?

- If you have to insert it into your vagina, are you comfortable with that?

If your partner won't use contraception when you want to, that's not OK. If you are in a situation where you feel unsafe or have been coerced into doing something you didn't want to do, seek support from a shelter or rape crisis centre as fast as you can.

Are there methods of contraception that aren't reliable?

YES. Withdrawal (when the penis is removed from the vagina before ejaculation) is extremely unreliable because some sperm is released before ejaculation. If 100 people use this method for contraception, 22 of them will become pregnant within a year. Douching also doesn't work and is not good for your vaginal health on top of that (see page 247). Sperm can't be removed reliably with a douche, and if those wily bastards have got past your cervix, no amount of douching will get them out.

STIs

STIs are no fun, but they are surprisingly common and they really don't have to be the end of the world. There's quite a few of them out there – from HPV to chlamydia to gonorrhoea. Many STIs are curable – although that's no excuse for not using appropriate protection. If you do have one, the important thing is to get the right treatment and then continue with life!

Having an STI doesn't necessarily mean that you can't have sex, but there are certain precautions you will need to take depending on what the situation is – for example, by using barrier-contraceptive methods or no-contact sex such as phone sex. Also, if you have an STI and you are about to have sex with someone, you must disclose this, and vice versa – you can always ask if they need to disclose anything to you. This information is an important part of consent as the person you're with needs to understand what level of risk they are comfortable taking and what type of protection to use. I know it can feel super awkward, but sharing information such as this is really important. If someone tells you they have an STI, respond without judgement – there's no reason to be embarrassed, and you don't want to prevent them from having this conversation again in the future.

For more info about STIs, check out the sex resources at the back of the book.

How to get tested

You can usually get an STI test at a sexual health clinic, doctor's surgery or pharmacy. There's no need to feel embarrassed when visiting – the people who work there have literally seen thousands of patients before you, so there's nothing they haven't seen before! When you're there, they may ask you some personal questions such as if you've had unprotected sex. It's important to answer honestly as they need this information in order to know what to test for.

At many clinics, you don't need to give them your real name. You may need to give them your correct contact details though if you need to wait a few days for your results.

Tests can come in different forms – you might have a blood test, a urine test, a genital swab or a physical examination. If you don't want to see a doctor for a test, you can get certain tests posted to your home.

The number of times you should get tested will vary depending on your lifestyle. It can range from up to every three months if you are sexually active with multiple partners to once a year if you're in a monogamous long-term relationship. However, if you are experiencing any symptoms (like foul-smelling discharge or sores); if you were using a condom and it broke or if you're entering a new monogamous relationship and want to stop using barrier methods, then go as soon as you can.

If you receive an STI diagnosis, you'll need to tell everyone you've had sex with recently. If you can't – perhaps you find it embarrassing (you shouldn't, but I get it) or there's a risk the person might react badly – there are loads of online services that will anonymously text the person or people with a message along the lines of 'Someone you've had sex with recently has had an STI diagnosis. Go get tested.'

Sex education for all

Was this the first time you learnt about some of this stuff? Are you about to go share this info with everyone you know because they probably didn't know about lots of it either? (Please do this – it would literally make me so happy.) Here's the thing: you shouldn't have had to learn it from a book (unless your parents/partner/teacher/friend gave it to you, in which case that person is extremely cool and you should keep them in your life forever). This stuff should be taught in all schools. Sex and/or relationships is something virtually every person will experience, and it's one of the most complex areas of our lives. Sex and relationship education (SRE) is **just as important** as teaching history or science, and it should be available to everyone.

What SRE should be

- It should cover pleasure – after all, that's the reason most people have sex. To leave pleasure out of sex education is like sending someone to culinary school and not teaching them how to make food tasty.

- LGBTQ+ issues can't be ignored – we have to stop assuming that cisgender heterosexual experiences are the only ones worth talking about.

- Consent must be a top priority – not just how to give it, but how to respect it.

- It must be anti-colonialist and anti-racist.

- People of all genders should learn the same things together.

- All contraceptive options should be taught – abstinence-only education doesn't work.

- It should be shame-free.

- It should show photos of vulvas – not just the internal gynaecological anatomy – and show body diversity!

- It must include masturbation and not imply that it's shameful.

The climax

I don't know what point of your sexual journey you are at right now. Perhaps you are only just beginning to discover more about your brilliant body and what brings you pleasure. Or maybe you are a total sexpert already. Either way, I hope this chapter has shown you the many wonders of the V and encouraged you to **put your pleasure first**. What could be more empowering – and a bigger middle finger to the kyriarchy – than you learning to love, embrace and celebrate your wonderful V and all the joy it brings.

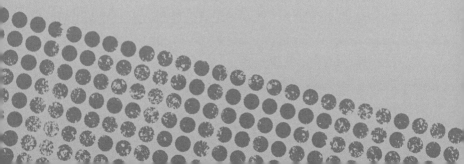

Chapter 4
WELCOME TO THE QUEERDOM

We've just talked about sex and pleasure – both wonderful ways to show your vulva some love! Now it's time to take it to the next level: let's double the vulva love and talk about people with vulvas who love other people with vulvas. Vulva love squared.

I am bisexual and love my darling LGBTQ+ community. It stands for:

Lesbian
Gay
Bisexual
Transgender
Queer/Questioning
+ = all the other identities.

Some people like to add I for Intersex and A for Asexual/ Aromantic. Don't worry, we'll be going through what these all mean very soon! Since we want to be as inclusive as possible (obvs!) and the acronym is starting to get a bit long, alternatives have been proposed like GSRD (Gender, Sexuality and Relationship Diversity).

Queer is a word that is often used as an umbrella term for the whole LGBTQ+ community. It's important to note that some people don't like the word queer because it has a history of being used as an insult. I totally understand. I grew up in the 90s when the word 'gay' was a slur that was used to describe unfashionable and shameful things. Older generations will remember queer being used in a similar way. Queer has been undergoing a reclamation process since the 1980s, starting during the AIDS crisis. I believe we must reclaim these words or the oppressors win.

As you probably know already, the world is not exactly 100 per cent accepting of queer love. There's often a societal assumption that everyone is heterosexual. Think about the relationships you see in media and culture – most are heterosexual, right? Or the way society talks about women and the way they look, usually in regard to how desirable they are to men. Or the way we never hear about queer history, which seems to imply everyone in the past was straight (completely false, btw).

Feminist writer Adrienne Rich described this system in her theory of compulsory heterosexuality (often abbreviated to comphet), in which heterosexuality is presumed and enforced on people, especially women. It explains everything I just talked about, as well as things such as arranged marriages and violence against queer people.

One of the ways compulsory heterosexuality works is by denying us knowledge and visibility of other forms of sexuality. So how can we resist this? Well, there are lots of things we can do, including strengthening LGBTQ+ rights and fighting discrimination. And, of course, more queer visibility!

LGBTQ+ visibility has been increasing rapidly the past few decades – more people are out as their true selves in society, and there are more of us queers on our screens, papers and mainstream media. And it's working: a 2015 YouGov poll showed 49 per cent of 18–24-year-olds in the UK don't identify as 100 per cent heterosexual, and I doubt that's because more people are queer! Instead, it's likely that more people feel comfortable being open about their queerness.

Because there's something we know for sure: there have always been queer people and there always will be. We've literally got lead tablets from second century-CE Egypt that detail how a woman can perform a love spell to make another woman fall in love with her.[24] Being queer is nothing new, and talking about queer history and the LGBTQ+ community after hundreds of years of erasure is a powerful and vital thing to do.

All the different ways to be queer

Ah, labels. For anyone who has newly come out, this is often one of the first big questions. Which label to use? And this itself is often quite a contentious question. Some people will be excited for the person coming out and will want to know which label they'll be selecting, and some won't understand why the label is so important at all. And before you know it, we're left wondering – are labels good or bad?

Well, it depends on you. You don't have to fit anyone's expectations, and you don't have to have a label. Taking one on is a personal choice. You also don't have to stick to one your whole life, but you absolutely can if you want to. Remember: you choose the label – it doesn't choose you.

24 Witches have always been queer icons.

LABELS CAN BE HELPFUL

- They can be a starting point for understanding your experiences because you can easily look to other people with the same label, for examples.

- They can help you find a community.

- They can be strategic – for example, it's easier to get legal rights if you have a clear message.

- Sexuality is often a huge part of a person's identity, and a label can be a symbol of pride.

- They can be a way of taking a political stand.

- It can be a springboard to helping you explore different parts of yourself.

LABELS CAN BE UNHELPFUL

- They can be too simplistic. Humans are more complicated than one-word descriptions.

- Identifying with a label can overshadow other equally important parts of your identity.

- Sexuality can change over time, so confining oneself to a label can be limiting.

- They can force Western labels on non-Western people.[25]

- They can lead people to assume that all people who use that label are the same.

- A label can feel exclusionary if you don't feel like you fit in with that community.

- A label can feel like a box.

25 A lot of the modern terms that I've listed reflect Western understanding of sexuality. Not all cultures understand sexuality in this way, and forcing a person to use a particular label may simply not reflect their culture.

Understanding your sexuality fully can take a while, but it's a beautiful journey to go on. It's not always easy to just point at a label and decide that one works for you. Just know that there's no rush, and you don't have to have it all worked out right now.

There are lots of different sexualities out there, which I think is amazing. It just goes to show how varied this glorious human race is. Here's some labels to explore – do you feel a connection to any of them?

- **Lesbian:** a woman or non-binary person who is only attracted to women.

- **Gay:** someone who is attracted to people of the same gender.

- **Bisexual:** someone who is attracted to two or more genders. It does not mean you think there are only two genders.

- **Pansexual:** someone who is attracted to people regardless of gender.

- **Polysexual:** someone who is attracted to many genders.

- **Asexual:** someone who does not experience sexual attraction.[26]

- **Aromantic:** someone who does not experience romantic attraction.[27]

- **Demisexual:** someone who does not experience sexual attraction until they have formed an emotional connection with someone.

- **Queer:** a general term for someone who isn't heterosexual.

- **Straight:** a woman who is only attracted to men or a man who is only attracted to women. This includes trans men and women.

26 The opposite of asexual is allosexual, if you were wondering.
27 Someone who is both asexual and aromantic is often abbreviated to 'aroace'.

Coming out – what is coming out?

The phrase 'coming out' has its origins in the British Empire. Originally, the phrase was used by high society. When young, upper-class women came of age in their late teens, they would 'come out' to the monarch at big elaborate balls to signify becoming a woman. Since the late 1800s, the phrase was appropriated by the queer community to mean someone new entering the community, often at drag balls, which was a subculture of big parties for the queer, particularly trans, community where people dressed and danced ostentatiously. It was a joyful process to find people like you and celebrate.

Nowadays, coming out has taken on a more general term to mean 'revealing' oneself not to be straight or cisgender (see page 8). Coming out is something that only exists because we live in a society where people are assumed to be straight or cis unless they say otherwise. But society is changing so fast – more and more people are identifying as queer, and one day I'd like to see us reach a place where coming out isn't necessary at all because no one assumes anything about people's sexuality or gender.

How to come out

There is no right or wrong way to come out. You can wait until you feel 100 per cent ready. You can tell some people but not others. You can shout about it from the rooftops, if that's your style! Every single person's coming out experience is unique and only you know what's best for you. Here are some tips if you're thinking about how to come out:

• Be sure that it's something you want to do, rather than something you feel like you're expected to do.

- Be prepared to answer questions, like 'what does this mean?' or 'how do you know?'

- You can tell everyone all at once – for example, by posting on social media – or you can do it person by person. News travels fast, so consider beforehand if there are any people you don't want to know (or to find out from someone else).

- If you're doing it in person, do it in a neutral, safe place so that you can leave if you need to.

- If you want to test the waters on how someone might react, suggest watching a queer movie or TV show together, such as *The Rocky Horror Picture Show*, *Carol*, *Moonlight* or *Dickinson*, and see what they say. You could also try initiating a conversation about an LGBTQ+ celebrity or ask what they think about LGBTQ+ issues and see how they react.

- Build a support network in advance filled with people you are confident will support you, such as friends, a trusted relative or a local LGBTQ+ group. Found families are just as valid as biological ones!

- If it doesn't go as well as you hoped, or you just want some extra support, there are loads of registered charities you can turn to, including the Switchboard LGBT+ Helpline, the Terrence Higgins Trust helpline and The Trevor Project. Or you can join an LGBTQ+ society at your school or uni if there is one (or you can start one!).

- Remember, their first reaction may not be how they really feel. Because we live in a kyriarchy, its values are often embedded deep within us and it takes work to unlearn these things. You may need to give them time to come around.

Coming out can be very liberating! Sometimes you have to take your time over it, but the relief and freedom can be an immense feeling! I know that it's not always 100 per cent safe for everyone to do this though, and it's my dearest wish that you have lots of people in your life who support you no matter what. I promise you, there are lots of people out there who love you.

A short history of some amazing queer people you should know about

As a teenager, I really struggled with how to express my queer identity. I knew from the moment I started going through puberty that I was bisexual, but I didn't really know what to do with this information. When I started dating, I had no idea where to even start getting romantic with women and non-binary people. But chatting up men? Easiest thing in the world. Looking back, I think it came from the fact that I didn't have a 'script' to be queer.

Growing up in a conservative religious community in a time before the internet had really taken off, I didn't know where to turn. On top of that, for much of my time as a child, there was a law in the UK called Section 28 that banned schools from teaching 'the acceptability of homosexuality as a pretended family relationship'. That was *literally* what the legislation said. Thankfully it was repealed in 2003, but it still had a huge knock-on effect. The enforced silence caused by this law and on my community meant I had no idea what it meant to be queer.

This is why representation is so important. Having examples – and hopefully role models – of queer people *just existing* as their true selves can provide a framework for others

on how to be their true selves. We are surrounded by stories of straight love and relationships from a very young age, and it can feel alienating and confusing. Representations of other forms of love, sex and relationships give us access to a script that speaks more to our experience, which we can copy until we feel comfortable to riff off it, personalize it, ad lib and even write an entirely new script of our own.

And that's why I want to spend a little time telling you about some amazing queer people. Their lives are interesting, difficult, inspirational and relatable. I wish I'd known about these people when I was younger. I had to live off the scraps of queerness I could find, such as *Xena: Warrior Princess*.[28] I'm so glad that you don't have to and you can have queer heroes (queeros?) galore.

The fight for queer acceptance – especially for women and people of marginalized genders – is nowhere near finished, and one of the most important ways we can stay hopeful is by learning about those who have come before.

If they can be happy, then so can we.

I've provided just short biographies, and if any of these people catch your eye, it would bring me untold joy if you went on to find out more.

28 Lucy Lawless, step on me.

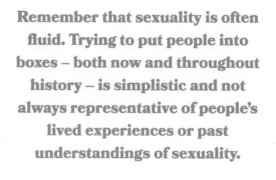

Remember that sexuality is often fluid. Trying to put people into boxes – both now and throughout history – is simplistic and not always representative of people's lived experiences or past understandings of sexuality.

Σαπφώ (Sappho) (c. 630–c. 570 BCE)

Sappho is the OG lesbian. Well, not really – lesbians definitely existed before her – but she had a huge impact. She was an ancient Greek poet – the first known female Greek poet in fact. Only fragments of her poems survived, and it may be because her work included love poems to other women and were actively destroyed.[29] Before lesbians were regularly called lesbians, they were named 'sapphists' after her. And do you know where the word lesbian comes from? Sappho was

born on the Greek island of . . . Lesbos. And the people who live there are known as Lesbians.

Josephine Baker (1906–1975)

Josephine Baker was a bisexual French-American performer, resistance fighter and civil rights activist. She was a sensation in Paris and was famous for her banana skirt costume. In the USA, she was regularly criticized in the press – the idea of a powerful, sophisticated Black woman was too horrifying for the powers that be to cope with in the 1930s. During WWII, she was recruited by French counter-intelligence to be a spy. Her celebrity meant that she could attend parties with important political and military

29 It could also have been because she wrote in a very early dialect of Greek that scholars had trouble understanding, so the debate's still open.

figures without too much suspicion, and she travelled round the world hiding secret letters in her underwear and writing messages in invisible ink on her sheet music. In the 1950s, she supported the civil rights movement in the US, fighting racial segregation by making speeches alongside Martin Luther King Jr and working with the civil rights organization NAACP. She had a number of marriages to various men and relationships with women, including Blues singer Clara Smith, jazz performer Ada 'Bricktop' Smith and author Collette.

Audre Lorde (1934–1992)

Audre Lorde was an American womanist[30] scholar, poet and lesbian. Born to Caribbean immigrants in New York, she dedicated her life to civil rights, supporting Black women and teaching round the world. She used her writing and poetry to communicate ideas about gender, race, class, disability, oppression, survival and beauty.

Frida Kahlo (1907–1954)

Frida Kahlo was a Mexican painter and one of the most important artists of her century. She taught herself to paint aged 18, after an accident confined her to bed for a few months and ultimately resulted in a lifelong disability. Her work often explored her relationship with her

---

30 Womanism is a term coined by author Alice Walker in 1979. Its definition has evolved since then, but generally today it focuses on the contributions of Black women to society.

body, gender and sexuality. She married fellow Mexican painter Diego Rivera and had a number of relationships with men and women throughout her life.

邱妙津 (Qiu Miaojin) (1969–1995)

Qiu Miaojin was a Taiwanese writer and filmmaker. Her work was avant-garde and explored themes of homoeroticism. Her book *Notes of a Crocodile* is the origin of both the Taiwanese slang word for lesbian: 拉子 (in Pinyin: lāzi) and the Chinese one also: 拉拉 (lālā), after the name of the main character.

Princess Catherine Hilda Duleep Singh (1871–1942)

Princess Singh was born in Suffolk to the last maharaja of the Sikh Empire, Maharaja Duleep Singh, and Ethiopian-German Maharani, Bamba Müller. She was a suffragist who fought for women's rights through peaceful campaigning. In the 1880s, she fell in love with German governess Lina Schäfer and they lived most of their lives together.

Claude Cahun (1894–1954) and Marcel Moore (1892–1972)

Claude Cahun was a French-Jewish photographer and artist, known for surrealist self-portraits that often played on gender. They famously said: 'Masculine? Feminine? It depends on the situation. Neuter is the only gender that always suits me.' They often collaborated with their lover and fellow artist, Marcel

Moore. In 1937, the two settled in Jersey, UK, to escape persecution, and when the Channel Islands were occupied by the Nazis, they joined the resistance.

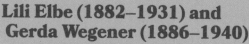

CLAUDE CAHUN & MARCEL MOORE

Lili Elbe (1882–1931) and Gerda Wegener (1886–1940)

Lili Elbe and Gerda Wegener were Danish painters, the former famous for her landscapes and the latter for portraits and lesbian erotica. They were married in 1904 after meeting as students in Copenhagen. Elbe is also known as one of the first people in the world to undergo gender-affirming surgery.

Bíawacheeitchish (c. 1800–1854)

Bíawacheeitchish was born to the A'aninin Nation and later adopted by a warrior of the Apsáalooke Nation (also known as the Crow Nation). She was two-spirit (see page 233) and a highly respected military leader. She had a number of wives, possibly between two and four.

BÍAWACHEEITCHISH

Queer as Folk

Two vulvas are better than one – at least in my world. Queer visibility is certainly on the rise, but there are still a lot of fights left to be fought. As I'm writing, there are 69 countries where it's illegal to be gay, with 11 of those countries carrying the death penalty as punishment. Conversion therapy (a form of 'therapy' – I use the word therapy very loosely here – to make someone straight or cis) is still legal in some countries, including the UK. And queer people are still at risk of so much violence.

Slowly but surely though, we're going in the right direction. In 1996, South Africa became the first country in the world to put in its constitution that people cannot be discriminated against because of their sexuality. Hopefully there will be even more positive change.

I am here to tell you, right here, right now that being a person with a V who loves other people with Vs is a **beautiful, wonderful, amazing** thing. If you are one of these people – or think you might be but aren't yet ready to come out – then just know I am here to welcome you with open arms when you are ready. I am overjoyed to have you as part of our vulva-love-squared club. And if you're not part of the club, we need allies more than ever, so I'm giving you some metaphorical pompoms to cheer us on.

No matter your sexuality, you are deserving of love, and that includes deserving to love yourself and your V. In the words of queer icon and writer Oscar Wilde,

'To love oneself is the beginning of a lifelong romance'.

Amazin LeThi (she/her)
Athlete, advocate, ambassador, author

Being a champion for change – on and off the field

In this piece, I reflect on the difficulties that Asian LGBTQ athletes still experience in not being able to celebrate being their authentic selves. Talking about bringing your whole self to the game is no longer enough. We need to talk about intersectionality, which, in my experience as an out Asian, means a multi-faceted mix of culture, identity, sexuality and biases. For many Asian athletes, the idea of stepping out on to the field as our authentic self for all to see induces a feeling of fear and even cultural shame and failure – we may have succeeded as a professional athlete but have shamed our family and community for not conforming to the norm.

Personally, I have experienced a tremendous amount of discrimination and bullying as an immigrant who is Asian and queer, growing up in an all-white area. Sports became my haven; it helped my mental health and gave me a sense of confidence and strength that eventually helped me learn to love myself and feel comfortable in exploring who I was. But in my formative years I struggled with my sexuality because I did not know how to express my feeling of difference, and I hadn't seen an Asian LGBTQ person or athlete in the media. And being the only Asian and queer person in sports came with the challenge of racism and homophobia.

Many athletes feel a sense of unity and support, particularly when playing team sports. But some Asian LGBTQ athletes have to deal with the double layer of racism and damaging stereotypes. This can prevent lots of us from participating in sports altogether. Thankfully, with the rise in LGBTQ athlete activism and the Black Lives Matter sports movement, many athletes and sports organizations are championing racial and sports equality.

My experiences growing up and seeing the lack of representation of out Asian LGBTQ athletes led me to the activism that I do today. My global work is built around challenging people to confront and dismantle the structures of racism and anti-LGBTQ hostility in sports. I collaborate with governments, Fortune 500 companies and sporting bodies focused on LGBTQ initiatives, looking at representation and inclusion and how we can continue to champion equality beyond the games and events.

On reflection, as a proud, unapologetic, visible queer Asian athlete, I realise the responsibility and power in sharing my story. My aim is to always send a positive and affirming message to all Asian LGBTQ athletes who may be currently struggling with their sexuality or gender identity – you are not alone. I became my best self through sports – I became the first Asian LGBTQ athlete in the world to hold the most ambassador roles, and to be an advisor to companies and organizations, and even political campaigns.

For me, Pride is not a month. It's an every day queer celebration to love ourselves and be an ally in action to the LGBTQ community. We can all be champions of change on and off the field.

Chapter 5

AND HER VULVA WAS WONDROUS TO BEHOLD

One of the most common things I get asked is why the vulva is so stigmatized. Look closely – there's something hidden in that question. It assumes that the vulva has always been stigmatized, and it's as though it's always been a fact of humanity that our bodies are reviled. But this isn't the case in the slightest! In fact, for thousands of years the vulva has been celebrated, revered and worshipped. The patriarchy has erased this history, and I'm here to set the record straight.

Around the world, different cultures, religions, folklores and myths have honoured and celebrated the vulva. It's time to unearth and celebrate this forgotten history so that we too can be part of a long tradition of vulva worship, admiration and celebration. **Vulvas are quite simply magical**.

Vulvas are where babies enter the world. The usual caveats apply that your worth is not tied to your fertility and our purpose is not to create babies – our purpose is whatever we want it to be. But imagine you lived in a pre-microscope, pre-ultrasound world. The fact that our bodies can create a whole new human from virtually nothing is pretty mind-blowing. In many religions, only gods can create life, so it stands to reason that **the vulva is divine**.

I love learning about different religions, cultures and folklore. I'm Jewish, and it's a part of me that I hold dearly. Religion has a huge impact on the world, and although many aspects of religion are steeped in misogyny, there are parts that are very beautiful. I know that religion can be very sacred to people, and my religion is very important to me. I also know it can sometimes be a bit difficult to talk about the V in relation to it, but I truly believe that the best way to honour something is to learn everything you can about it.

The vulva is divine

The universe and you

Christianity, like many other religions, is often tarnished with a brush of being anti-sex and misogynistic. For instance, Tertullian (c. 155–c. 220 CE), one of the earliest Christian thinkers from what is now Tunisia, believed women were 'the devil's gateway' due to the sin of Eve.[31]

But, as with most things, it's way more complicated than that. Christianity is 2,000 years old and there have been over two billion Christians alive throughout history, so painting an entire religion with one brush just doesn't work.

There have been loads of powerful women and positive female figures in Christianity, especially in medieval Europe. Hildegard of Bingen (1098–1179 CE) was a German nun – and a massive overachiever. She wrote books, music, plays, was a herbalist, went on speaking tours, corresponded with popes and emperors and founded two nunneries. To say she was a celeb of her time is an understatement.

In her book *Scivias*, she wrote about the divine revelations she received from God. In one of them, she learnt the shape of the universe. This is what it looked like:

31 Lots of theologians argue that the fruit eaten by Eve from the tree of knowledge was actually a metaphor for sex; the knowledge was 'carnal knowledge'; and the original sin wasn't eating the forbidden fruit but actually sex (snakes are very phallic – it makes sense!).

She said it was 'in the shape of an egg', but I think there's little doubt that she actually meant a vulva. This was a woman who unquestionably knew what a vulva looked like – not only was she well-versed in medicine, she wrote the first-known written description of the female orgasm:

> **When a woman is making love with a man, a sense of heat in her brain, which brings with it sensual delight, communicates the taste of that delight during the act and summons forth the emission of the man's seed. And when the seed has fallen into its place, that vehement heat descending from her brain draws the seed to itself and holds it, and soon the woman's sexual organs contract.**

It's pretty heteronormative, but that's probably because she was writing for a public audience, and she had to play by the Church's rules. (It's unlikely people would have bought her books if she was like, 'I'm a massive lezzo' – even though there's evidence she had a romantic relationship with another female nun called Richardis von Stade. Either way, I'm pretty confident that Hildegard would have known that what she was drawing looked like a vulva . . .)

And the idea that the universe is a vulva is not limited to just one woman from 900 years ago. In Hinduism, the oldest religion in the world, the *yoni* – the Sanskrit word for the womb and vulva – is often described as 'the origin of everything'.

Let's take a quick step back for a moment – unlike other religions, Hinduism doesn't have a central text (such as the Bible for Christianity), nor does it have a founder, nor a central set of teachings. It's an immensely diverse set of philosophies, ceremonies, mythologies and texts. It's worth bearing this in mind, as it means there's no 'definitive' set of interpretations or beliefs.

The branch of Hinduism called Shaktism believes that our literal reality is a woman. Or more specifically, one woman – Shakti. Shakti is a goddess, but rather than her simply being a person with powers, she is cosmic energy itself: a yoni and the source of the universe. It's believed by many that when she joined with her husband Shiva, who is the lingam (a penis, but again lots of big cosmic stuff going on), the universe sprang forth. She is the source of all creation, the energy that gives things life, and it is believed that when we die, we shall return into her. **The vulva is literally the universe**.

The goddess within

The concept of the vulva being a goddess is thousands of years old, and I'm literally so excited to tell you about my bae, Ishtar. Ishtar, sometimes called Inanna, is an ancient Mesopotamian goddess of sex and war.[32] She's described as the queen of heaven, goddess of Venus (the planet) and protector of the ancient city of Uruk in modern-day Iraq, founded about 6,000 years ago. She is the origin of goddesses Venus and Aphrodite, the OG deity of sexiness.

As a goddess, her vulva was a huge part of her whole thing. It's quite literally holy.[33] A story called 'Inanna and the God of Wisdom' opens in this way:

> **Inanna placed the shugurra, the crown of the steppe, on her head...**
> **When she leaned against the apple tree, her vulva was wondrous to behold.**
> **Rejoicing at her wondrous vulva, the young woman Inanna applauded herself.**

Can we just pause for a minute? I think we should all applaud our vulvas more. Go on – put this book down and give yourself a standing ovary-ation (that's a terrible pun – I apologize).

---

32 Interestingly, although she is the goddess of sex, she isn't that tied to human fertility and is rarely shown as a mother and more often as a warrior. If you're confused about how sex and war go together, one academic hilariously described her as 'the goddess of adrenaline'.

33 Or 'holey'... geddit?!

Right, where were we? So, in that passage, the goddess is crowning herself the queen of the land, and her vulva both receives and gives power to the earth, particularly its fertility. We see this in the story of her wedding to the god of shepherds, Dumuzi. On their wedding night, she says to him 'my vulva is full of eagerness' and asks, 'Who will plough my vulva?' And he replies dutifully, 'I will plough your vulva!' While they have sex, the land around them flourishes and the crops grow tall. The whole rest of the story is about how she is so happy and sexually satisfied at how he laid his hands on her 'holy vulva'.[34]

And Ishtar worship actually lives on today. In Judaism, there's a spring festival called פּורים/Purim. Purim celebrates the time the Jewish people survived an attempted genocide in Persia by villain of the story, Haman, adviser to the king. It's literally my favourite holiday, and we put on fancy dress, drink copious amounts of alcohol, give food and money to the less fortunate and generally celebrate being alive. A festive Purim food is *hamantaschen*, a triangular biscuit traditionally filled with poppyseeds. As children, we're told that the biscuit represents Haman's ear – but who has triangular ears? – or his hat. And what ancient Persian wore a tricorn hat? You obviously know where I'm going with this – look at that biscuit! Triangle? Vulva. Poppyseeds? Pubic hair. You can't unsee it.

153

And there's evidence to support the theory that hamantaschen originated in worship to Ishtar's vulva: in the Book of Jeremiah, written around the sixth century BCE, Jeremiah is getting annoyed because all the Jews are worshipping other gods. He complains:

> **seest thou not what they do in the cities of Judah and in the streets of Jerusalem? . . . the women knead their dough, to make cakes to the queen of heaven.**

And who is the Queen of Heaven? Only our babe Ishtar. Hamantaschen may well be a cake for her and her holy vulva

And I'll add more clues: in the Purim text, the Megillah, the leading lady is called Esther. It's theorized that the name Esther is derived from the name Ishtar. Rabbi Nehemiah – who lived in the second century CE – also said that Esther meant 'Venus'. Remember which goddess is associated with Venus? Next Purim, look up a hamantaschen recipe and make your own vulva cookie! Make me some too?[35]

> **Fun fact: the translation above is from the King James Bible. King James VI of Scotland/I of England was super queer and had relationships with the men in his court. I just really needed you to know that a queer man commissioned this translation of the Bible.**

35 It's also possible that hamantaschen originated in the worship of Asherah, the wife of Yahweh (who the monotheistic God may have originated from) before Judaism was monotheistic. She was also called the Queen of Heaven. But there's a possibility that Asherah and Ishtar are connected.

My body is a temple

Vulva temples are obviously my favourite kind of place, and they feature all over the world, from India to Mexico City.[36] There's a famous story about the Hindu god Daksha, who organized a big event where sacrifices would be made. He invited all the gods, goddesses, kings and important people of the world. But he didn't invite his daughter Sati or her husband Shiva. (He really hated his son-in-law . . . it's a whole thing.) Sati couldn't believe her own father wouldn't invite her and assumed that it was just expected that she'd be there. But when they arrived, a fight broke out (extremely relatable family drama). Sati couldn't bear the fighting any more and she took her life by throwing herself into the sacrificial fire.[37]

After waging a little war, Shiva was so saddened by his wife's death that he took her body and wandered across the land. The god Vishnu cut up her body and placed pieces down where they wandered. Each place where some of her body fell is now a Shakti Pitha, a shrine. Where her yoni fell in Assam, the temple of Kamakhya was built. Kamakhya is a goddess herself, and once a year at the temple, a festival called Ambubachi Mela is held. This summer festival celebrates the annual menstruation of the goddess (lucky – imagine having a period just once a year!). During her 'flow', the temple is closed for three days, then on the fourth day it's opened and all the pilgrims who have come to celebrate receive a symbolic piece of red cloth. Her menstruation is important for the fertility of the land, and as she so kindly gives the earth her blood, blood must be returned to her in the form of an animal sacrifice.

So remember, kids: **vulvas are goddesses** – bow down to their almighty power.

36 The Basilica of Our Lady of Guadeloupe in Mexico City has a very famous depiction of the Virgin Mary who appeared to a Chichimec man, which many Mexican feminists have pointed out may represent a vulva.

37 Don't worry, she was later reincarnated into Parvati.

The holy vulva

Vulvas may represent many goddesses, but there's a man associated with a lot of vulva imagery that I can't not tell you about. Prepare to have your mind blown, I'm talking about the big guy – Jesus.

When Jesus was crucified, he got five holy wounds: one on each hand, one on each foot and one on his side where a soldier poked him with a lance to make sure he was dead. And this wound is often depicted in prayer books as a red, pointed oval. Very vulvic. And the similarity was not lost on medieval Christians.

 Not only did the wound bleed – adding to the vulva-ness; it was also associated with birth. During labour, some people would wrap a birthing girdle – which is basically a long strip of parchment with prayers, invocations and illustrations to protect the wearer during such a dangerous moment – around their belly. The holy side wound was often depicted on it, marking the association between it and the V.

The wound is also often – ahem – penetrated in stories and art. When Jesus was resurrected, the apostle Thomas just couldn't believe it, so to make sure it was really him, he put his finger in the side wound. Thomas, *please*.

This pointed oval shape is a recurring motif in Christian imagery and is called a 'mandorla' (Italian for almond). The shape is constructed by overlapping two circles, making what's called a vesica piscis.[38] The vesica piscis was used in Gothic architecture to make doors, arches and windows – yes, those pointed church doors are secret vulvas. The mandorla shape is most often used to surround holy people in religious iconography, almost like a full body halo. It's sometimes interpreted as a gateway between the human/physical world

---

38 The vesica piscis is a symbol that is much older than Christianity, and it's first-known appearance is in the work of mathematician Euclid, who lived in Egypt in 300 BCE.

and the divine/spiritual world, but some believe it's a representation of the cycle of birth and rebirth. Or it could be representing Mary's womb and how it brought Jesus into the world. Basically, big V vibes.

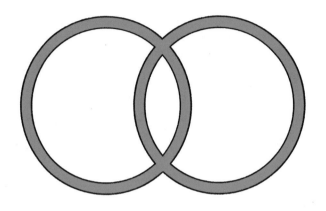

The vulva is a ward against evil

Demon, be gone

Move over Buffy the Vampire Slayer – vulvas can literally scare off demons. On church eaves and walls all over Europe, especially in Ireland, there are carvings of people dramatically holding open their vulvas for worshippers passing by on their way to Sunday prayers. These carvings, called Sheela-na-gigs, were made between the 12th and 16th centuries, and no one knows why they're there.

They are such a mystery that no one even knows what the name means or what they symbolize. The main theory is that these were made at a time when people in Europe followed a combination of paganism and Christianity. Sheelas could represent the hag goddess, the Cailleach, who is associated with the weather, winter and nature. Since they are often above windows and doors, her vulva display could be there to keep evil from entering, as tradition suggests that demons can't stand the sight of the vulva.

In the 17th century, the French folklorist Jean de La Fontaine published a story called 'The Devil of Pope-Fig Island', which features just that.[39] Pope-Fig Island is a godforsaken place ruled by devils, and all the people who live there are awful. One day, a devil comes to a farmer and demands that he gives him half of all his crops to sell, so he can make loads of money. The farmer tricks the devil by giving him the roots of the corn and the leaves of the carrots (basically the worthless bits). The devil goes to the market but is laughed at, which makes him furious. He realizes he's been tricked, and is like, 'I'm going to beat that farmer for what he's done! But first I've got an appointment to ravish this other guy's wife, so I'll see you in a week. THEN YOU'LL BE SORRY!' The farmer goes crying to his wife, Perretta, because he doesn't know what to do. And she's like, 'I'll take care of it, hun.' So, he goes to hide in a vase of holy water (try getting him there, demon!) and when the devil arrives at their house, Perretta runs up to him wailing about how her husband is a brute, saying:

He'd with his claws your lordship tear and slash;
(translation: my husband is super violent!)
See, only see, my lord, he made this gash;
(pointing to her vulva, calling it a wound)

39 It's based on a 16th-century story originally by French writer Rabelais in his book *Gargantua and Pantagruel*, so don't go thinking he came up with it.

On which she showed – what you will guess, no doubt;
(just say vulva, it's OK!)
And put the demon presently to rout;
(this means the devil retreated in terror)
Who crossed himself and trembled with affright.
(he's freaked)
He'd never seen nor heard of such a sight.
(because he's apparently never seen a vulva?!)

The devil runs off, terrified, and everyone, including the clergy, compliments Perretta on her terribly clever plan. Although it's odd that the devil had never seen a vulva before (especially because he's always talking about being a ladies' man), it's still pretty incredible that a vulva was powerful enough to scare off the devil.

All's fair in love and war

The practice of 'anasyrma' – or lifting up the skirt to expose your genitals – is just as powerful as it sounds.

The ancient Greek philosopher Plutarch once wrote a tale about when the Persian army rose up against the Medes, an ancient people who lived in modern-day Iran. The women of the city saw their men returning after clearly having lost and were having none of it. They lifted up their skirts and said (I'm paraphrasing here): 'Where TF are you running to, cowards? You come to crawl back up our vaginas, you little babies!' And the soldiers, having been told what's what, went back to fight and won the war, courtesy of some new-found confidence.

Sisters are doing it for themselves

Sometimes though, you've got to do the work of protecting your loved ones yourself. There's a story that goes that one day, Pele, the goddess of volcanoes and creator of the islands of Hawaii, was out and about when the half-hog, half-man

Kamapua'a tried to force himself on her. Her sister Kapo could sense her distress from afar and did what all good sisters do – detached her vulva from her body and sent it flying through the air to her aid. He was so distracted that he left Pele in search of the flying vulva. The place where the vulva fell is said to be Kohelepelepe, a huge crater on the island of Oahu. And because of this, she is also known as 'Kapo-kohe-lele' or 'Kapo with the travelling vulva'.

Is there anything the vulva can't do? Next time you need to win a battle, call on the V.

The vulva is powerful

Mother nature

Pliny the Elder (c. 23–79 CE) was an ancient Roman natural philosopher[40] who wrote what might be the first-ever encyclopaedia, called *Natural History*. He made some pretty wild assertions, such as telling people that bear cubs are born as lumps of white flesh and their mother has to lick them into the shape of a bear. In the chapter 'Facts connected with the menstrual discharge', he writes:

> **There is no limit to the marvellous powers attributed to females. For, in the first place, hailstorms, they say, whirlwinds, and lightning even, will be scared away by a woman uncovering her body while her monthly courses are upon her.**

The idea that vulvas can be used to control nature is a long-standing folk myth. There's a Korean folktale about a group of sisters-in-law who were herb-picking when a tiger attacked them. The youngest bravely offered to distract the tiger while

40 Old-timey name for scientist before the scientific revolution in the 1500s.

the other two ran away. But she was so scared, she turned her back on the tiger, took off her clothes and leaned forward in the hopes it would make her death easier. But when the tiger saw a big vertical 'mouth', surrounded by hair and dripping with blood, he mistook it for a fearsome creature. The tiger ran off in such a fright it accidentally fell off a cliff and died.

I think the link between the power of the V and nature comes from a deep-seated understanding that it's a place where so much life – and death – can happen.

My, what big teeth you have

Penis-havers around the world, you'd better be careful. This pussy bites back.

All over the world, there are stories of vaginas with teeth. They're usually pretty sad stories, though – often the vaginal teeth are unwanted by the owner, and a man has to knock them out. This type of 'vagina dentata' myth typically stems from a fear of female sexuality, implying it's dangerous and must be controlled. It's also about the anxiety of castration and emasculation. As long as the patriarchy has been around, this has been one of its biggest fears.

But some of these types of myths have been a force for positive change. For example, every April since 1969, in Kawasaki, Japan, the Kanamara Matsuri festival takes place. It commemorates a folk tale about a local blacksmith who made an iron dildo to help a woman remove the teeth from her vagina so that she could have sex unimpeded. During the festival, there is a procession of mini Shinto shrines of comically giant penises paraded around the streets, alongside penis- and vulva-shaped food. Nowadays, all the money raised by the festival goes to HIV research.

And sometimes the trope is subverted. In Māori folklore, the goddess Hine-nui-te-pō once used her vaginal teeth to protect herself from the trickster Māui.[41] Māui's father had told his son that he would be defeated by the goddess of death, Hine-nui-te-pō. Māui wanted to prove him wrong, so he decided to take it upon himself to defeat the goddess of death himself and bring humanity the gift of immortality. To do this, he planned to climb up the vagina of the giant goddess and climb out of her mouth.[42] By reversing the process of birth, he would kill the goddess, and death would never happen again. He waited until she was asleep and asked the birds around him to not laugh at the strange sight they were about to witness. But as he started to climb inside her vagina, the tīrairaka (fantails), couldn't hold it in! They burst into laughter, which woke the goddess up, and she quickly felt what was happening. She used the obsidian teeth in her vagina to crush him to death.

Of course, there's no basis in truth of these stories – there never really has been a person with teeth in their vagina capable of killing or castrating someone – but the fact that these stories exist demonstrates just how powerful people throughout history have believed the V to be.

The vulva is fun

A laughing matter

We all get gloomy sometimes and need cheering up. And who better than a friend to make you laugh? And what better than with a vulva?

In a story from the eighth-century collection of Japanese myths 古事記 (Kojiki), vulvas make a delightful appearance. After an argument with her brother, the sun goddess, 天照大身神

41 Yes, the one from the Disney movie *Moana*. Not sure why they didn't use this tale as part of the plot?

42 It was believed all over the world that the vagina was physically connected to the nose and mouth.

(Amaterasu), shuts herself away in a cave to sulk. But, being the goddess of the sun, that meant the world was plunged into darkness. This was obviously not good, so all the gods gathered to try to lure her out and restore light to the world. They tried everything they could think of – they made the cockerels crow in the hopes it would bring dawn, made offerings, and said prayers and solemn words. Then アメノウズメ (Ame-no-Uzume), goddess of dawn and mirth, had an idea. She gathered up her clothes and 'became divinely possessed, exposed her breasts and pushed her skirt band down to her genitals'. All the gods started laughing at her dancing, and Amaterasu wanted to see what the hysterics were all about, so she poked her head out from the cave. They quickly grabbed her to pull her out, and light was restored to the world. What an achievement – imagine being able to say, 'If it weren't for my vulva, we'd be in eternal night'!

This might seem like a pretty out-there story, but it's not even Japan-specific – goddesses are often cheered up at the sight of a vulva. In ancient Greece, the goddess of agriculture, Δημήτηρ (Demeter), was in mourning after her daughter Persephone was abducted by Hades, god of the underworld. She went in search of her, and came across the town of Eleusis. A local woman, Baubo, invited her in for food and drink, but Demeter refused because she was just too sad to eat (been there, babe). Baubo decided to try a different tactic to win her over. She lifted up her dress, and 'then the goddess fixes her eyes upon these [her vulva], and is pleased with the strange form of consolation. Then becoming more cheerful after laughing, she takes and drinks off the draught spurned before.' In ancient Greek art, Baubo is often depicted either with her legs splayed with a big vulva on show or her face is literally the vulva.

If I am ever sad, I give you full permission to lift your skirt at me.

Vulva is the new pink

In medieval Europe, it was very popular to go on a pilgrimage to a holy place, such as a shrine or a church, that housed a saintly relic – there would often even be a gift shop where you could buy a souvenir. But rather than something saying 'I saw Jesus's finger bone and all I got was this lousy T-shirt', you'd get a lead or pewter badge, which you'd wear on your clothes or fix to the top of your walking stick. It was quite the fashion statement.

Some of the badges were – let's say – erotic in nature. No one knows why they were like this though, as it was never written down. They might have been used to ward off the plague, to invoke fertility or simply just as a funny souvenir to show the lads at home. They could also have existed because in medieval Christianity, they were super into the idea of birth and rebirth, and of course vulvas are a big part of that. My fave theory is that they were there to show that someone is on pilgrimage. At the end of a pilgrimage, all your sins are forgiven. So what's the logical conclusion? Get some sinning in on the way. Basically, the badge could have been a sign that the wearer was up for some no-strings-attached-sexy-fun-times.

The badge illustrated is from around the 14th or 15th century, and it would have been a familiar scene to people at the time. It appears to be parodying the medieval Catholic tradition of parading around icons and relics (yes, just like the Shinto festival!). The vulva is, indeed, a holy relic. You can buy replicas of these badges nowadays, and I highly recommend it as a modern symbol of vulva pride.

Give your vulva a round of applause

You may think these myths, stories and legends are a thing of the past, but the power of the vulva is very much here with us today.

In 1958, Kom women in modern-day Cameroon used the centuries-old practice of *anlu* to protest British colonial forces selling off their farmland and overregulating agriculture. Anlu is when groups of women gather together to shame someone who's done something wrong. They bare their vulvas to the people responsible, dance, scream and shriek. As part of anlu, any woman who hears the shriek must stop whatever she is doing and join the demonstration. Baring their vulvas is a powerful act, as Kom men believe that such is the power of a vulva that seeing one is an ill omen. And Kom women don't have any qualms about using that power to their advantage – as well as the vulval demonstration and fearsome dancing, they set up roadblocks, disrupted courts of law, markets and schools; turned the yards of politicians' homes into toilets; and even held mock burials for the people they wanted to take down. The demonstration lasted for three years and was immensely successful, ending up resulting in a new government being elected in 1961.

Sixty years later, the US erupted into protests following George Floyd's murder by police in Minneapolis. A photo of the Portland protests by *The Oregonian* journalist Dave Killen, which went viral for its vulval display, showed how much power the vulva still has, even now. One night, a woman wearing nothing bar a face mask and a hat passed the photographer to confront a line of riot police. She bared herself to them to confront them in their violence, and they shot at her foot with rubber bullets, which hit so hard she bled. She sat down in front of the riot police and spread her legs wide for them to see all. A fellow protester came to shield her from the rubber bullets, but she sidestepped him and continued to bare herself. The anonomous woman, who has spoken about the experience, revealed the act was to say: 'Shoot this, look at this!'

The vulva is wondrous and powerful to behold. The vulva is a goddess and the universe. The vulva can make people laugh and make people run in fear. Sometimes it can feel like the V has been stigmatized forever, but this couldn't be further from the truth. For thousands of years, humanity has revered its might. Between your legs, you have a power beyond reason. And just like Ishtar, we should all applaud it a lot more.

Chapter 6

GEORGIA O'KEEFFE PAINTED FLOWERS, OK?!

VENUS DE HOHLE FELS

The oldest-known depiction of a human is a 40,000-year-old, 6-cm-long figurine carved from a woolly mammoth tusk, called the *Venus of Hohle Fels*. She stands with her hands resting under large breasts above a big belly. She has wide hips with legs ending in a point, and in place of a head, a little carved loop, suggesting it was worn as a pendant. And, of course, the part I'm most interested in: a huge vulva. She was discovered in 2008 by a team of archaeologists from the University of Tübingen. In their paper, they describe her as 'oversized' and 'exaggerated', with an 'extreme emphasis on sexual attributes and lack of emphasis on the head, face and arms and legs'.

Can we take a step back? Is this an exaggerated body shape? Her body reminds me of gorgeous and TOTALLY REAL people, such as Lizzo and Sofie Hagen. It's not exactly photo-realistic, but I don't think stylization necessarily means it's not representative – but that's an art debate for another day. The archaeologists say there's no emphasis on the arms, but the fingers and arms are clearly carefully carved out. They write that these types of figurines from the Palaeolithic era are an 'expression of fertility' and insist 'this is about sex'. But she's literally just standing there. If she was engaged in sex, or even in a sexy pose, maybe I'd agree – but she's JUST STANDING THERE. These men consider this woman to be sexual, literally just by her existence. It's a very androcentric (meaning focused on men) way of looking at it, as it assumes it is for male pleasure. Is there any actual evidence it was made for a man? Spoiler: no.

Compare this to the painting *Benefits Supervisor Sleeping* by Lucian Freud – one of my all-time favourite paintings. It depicts a fat woman asleep on a sofa. These two women have a very similar body shape, but I don't think Freud's has ever been described as sexual.

Why is a 40,000-year-old woman's body considered sexual, but the same body, just in modern times, is not? I think the difference lies in what we assume about society across time. We like to assume people living tens of thousands of years ago were led by their genitals and their stomachs and nothing else – even though there's literally no evidence to support that. We assume the *Venus* is sexual because we assume they could think of nothing but sex. We assume the *Benefits Supervisor* is not sexual because we've 'moved on from that' and find a 'better' body type sexual (those quote marks are doing some heavy lifting here – see the fatphobia section on page 41).

This is why feminism is so important – our art history is being forced into narrow interpretations by the patriarchy. Professors Catherine Hodge McCoid and Leroy D. McDermott have put forward a very compelling theory that the reason the Venus figurines (the *Venus of Hohle Fels* is one of many) look 'exaggerated' to the male archaeologists is that they are used to looking at women straight on. But if you look at the Venuses from top down, as though you are Venus herself, it suddenly looks very accurate. They compared photos of a woman's body from her own point of view with photos of the figurines from the same angle, and they matched remarkably. **These figurines weren't made by horny men: they were self-portraits.**

Art has a huge influence on different cultures. One of the best ways to understand what a society or community thinks is to look at their art. You can probably think of only a handful of examples of vulvas in art off the top of your head – what could I possibly have to write about in this chapter? But there are so many that I could write an entire book just on this. In fact, for thousands of years, artists have been venerating the V. They have sung, written, sculpted, painted and performed about the V. We have a lot to learn from them, and if they can love the V enough to create entire artworks out of them, then we can celebrate it unashamedly, and we can become proud of ourselves and know our bodies are something to glorify.[43]

---

43 I've tried to find examples of trans and intersex people in art, but because of discrimination and erasure, they are few and hard to find. I hope society can address this imbalance by fostering new artists from marginalized groups and funding more feminist art history research. I have also tried to include indigenous art and art of oppressed peoples, but because of colonialism, much of it has been violently erased. There is also much art that only exists in the oral tradition or is ephemeral, which I, by its nature, don't have access to.

Bringing people together

Vulvas have brought people together since the dawn of time. This powerful body part has always been at the centre of human culture and a building block for community. The 'Art Gallery' in Carnarvon Gorge, Australia, is a huge sandstone wall with paintings and carvings that are at least 10,000 years old. There's a section that's just loads and loads of vulvas. There are way too many for it to have been done by one person – this had to have been a community effort by local Indigenous people. Why they are there, and why there are so many, no one knows. Ancient vulva walls have been seen all over the world, from Bolivia and Turtle Island[44] to Brazil and Spain. Vulvas also feature heavily in rock art from Rapa Nui[45] and are called 'komari'.

Fast-forward ten millennia, and the V is still a uniting focal point of society. During the 2015 Republican presidential campaign in the US, then-candidate Donald Trump was questioned by news anchor Megyn Kelly during a debate about previous sexist comments he'd made. Trump was so emotional about the line of questioning that in a later interview he complained: 'you could see there was blood coming out of her eyes, blood coming out of her wherever'. The implication? She was menstruating and moody. There was a huge backlash and in response, artist Sarah Levy collected her menstrual blood in a menstrual cup and used it to paint a portrait of him called *Whatever (Bloody Trump)*. Using blood to paint his face shows how it's really *him* who's been overcome with anger and bloodlust. He should never have underestimated how referring to the V would bring people together.

44 Turtle Island is the indigenous name for North America.
45 Rapa Nui is the indigenous name for Easter Island, off the coast of Chile.

All the wonders of the world

The V is a wondrous, beautiful body part and artists have long been using the subject to inspire body confidence.

In 2006, Brighton-based artist Jamie McCartney read about the huge increase in labiaplasties, realized how much genital shame contributed to this and resolved to make an artwork of 400 vulval casts to showcase the amazing vulva diversity out there. He published a book with photos of all the casts (one of my favourite games is to flip through it with a friend and try and spot which one looks most like ours). The diversity is huge – it features vulvas of different shapes and sizes; ones from people with medical conditions such as lichen sclerosus and cancer; vulvas pre- and post-birth; and vulvas of trans people who have undergone genital reconstruction surgery. The artwork is now recommended by many doctors to patients who come to them requesting cosmetic labiaplasties to demonstrate the huge natural variation of vulval appearance and to spread the positive message of vulva diversity.

Sometimes, though, you have to get up-close and personal to really highlight the message. Annie Sprinkle – sexologist, sex worker and artist extraordinaire – did just that in the 1990s, with her 'Public Cervix Announcement'. She invited visitors to view her cervix by putting a speculum in her vagina and giving the audience a torch to take a good look. She started this work because she realized that most people go their whole lives never seeing a cervix – even though they entered the world through one – and wanted to provide an opportunity for people to view one at least once in their lifetime. She says the aim was to help lift a veil of ignorance and assure people that the vagina 'has no teeth'.

Like Sprinkle, midwife Ina May Gaskin also wanted to celebrate the V and did so through her art by showcasing one of the most powerful things a vagina can do, with absolutely no apology. The 2008 photograph *Terese in Ecstatic Childbirth* shows a woman giving birth and experiencing what is known as 'birth ecstasy'. The work challenges the idea that childbirth is universally traumatizing. Many people have found this image uncomfortable – when the Birth Rites Collection went on tour in 2008 (showing this photograph among others), the Glasgow Science Centre absolutely refused to have it at the entrance of the exhibition. Instead, they suggested a drawing of a forceps delivery.[46] The implication was that an image of childbirth is only acceptable to be viewed if the body is medicalized and in pain. But this photograph sets the record straight.

Part of a long tradition

Don't be fooled into thinking celebratory V art is a modern phenomenon.

Dancing Girl is a sculpture from c. 2500 BCE, from the Indus Valley civilization in modern-day Pakistan. The vulva is well defined and uncovered, and she stands proudly and confidently. Clearly, neither she nor her makers had any problem with bared vulvas.

But when you think of Western sculpture, the image that usually comes to mind is the total opposite – one of ancient Greek women sporting hidden-away, Barbie-doll vulvas. That all started with ancient Greek sculptor Praxiteles and his

---

46 Forceps are metal instruments for assisting birth that clamp on to a baby's head like a claw machine at the arcade.

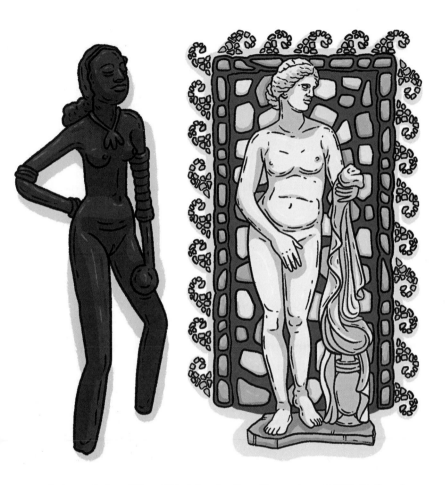

sculpture *Aphrodite of Knidos* (*c.* fourth century BCE). Before he came along, women in Greek sculpture generally were clothed because nudity was something associated with divinity, and women were canonically inferior to men in ancient Greek civilization.[47] Praxiteles was clearly feeling adventurous when he made two versions of Aphrodite coming out of a bath – one clothed, one naked. He went off to sell his work, and the temple of Aphrodite in Kos took the clothed one (they didn't want people to think they were pervs), and the Knidos temple took the other (they were chiller about the whole naked-lady thing).

47 Aristotle has a lot to answer for.

The naked one turned out to be very popular and word of her scandal and beauty spread fast. Legend goes that even the gay men of Greece liked her because she looked like a man from behind and they loved that butt. That might be why she was a bit more acceptable and paved the way for female nudes – her body was considered masculine. And so, the V entered the Greek scene.

I wish we could go back in time and ask people what they thought about the V, but until then we have to make do with looking at their objects. The Moche civilization, which flourished in modern-day Peru around 100–800 CE, produced a huge amount of ceramics, many of which had a sexual theme. Most of the examples we have nowadays survived because they were looted from their original sites by colonizers.

What we can tell from the sexy Moche pots is very interesting. The pots depict anal sex, blow jobs, masturbation . . . but very little penis-in-vagina sex. Colonizers at the time used this as 'proof' of the degeneracy of non-Western cultures, but now I hope we can look at the same thing and think of something very different. What it tells us is that penis-in-vagina sex was not necessarily the 'natural' way to have sex. Human sexual culture has always been rich and varied, and we shouldn't feel shame for finding joy in what society would have us believe are 'non-traditional' acts.

Of course, art and sex have always gone hand in hand. In Japanese culture, 春画 (shunga) is a genre of erotic art, most popular during the Edo period (1603–1867). The most famous work is *The Dream of the Fisherman's Wife* (1814) by 葛飾 北斎

(Katsushika Hokusai).[48] It depicts a woman being eaten out by an octopus – and honestly, you gotta be pretty confident of your V to let a squid near it. Shunga was used as pornography, but it was also a form of sex education and protection for the house from evil spirits, much like Sheela-na-gigs.

SO THE IDEA THAT THE VULVA HAS ALWAYS BEEN OPPRESSED AND MADE INVISIBLE IS JUST NOT TRUE! FOR THOUSANDS OF YEARS, ART HAS CELEBRATED VULVAS.

48 Yes, the same guy who made that famous Japanese print of a wave, *The Great Wave Off Kanagawa*. A fun fact to trot out when you see your auntie has a new phone case with *The Great Wave* on it.

Is it a V or is it a scandal?

Georgia O'Keeffe is generally considered to be the mother of American modernism,[49] and she painted a very famous series of flower artworks, which have a certain . . . theme. *Many of them are very vulvic-looking.* But she always insisted they were just flowers. She may have said this because it's the truth, but it could also have been because homosexuality was illegal in the US at this time. She was queer and had a number of relationships with women, so may have been trying to protect herself from legal scrutiny – especially because she was married to a man at the time, which would have only added to the scandal. We'll probably never know the truth, so you'll have to decide for yourself.

49 Modernism was an art movement in the early 20th century that sought to reflect the realities of modern life.

O'Keeffe's flower paintings may have been metaphoric, but often vulvas in paintings are very explicit – and just as divisive. *L'Origine du monde* (1866) by Gustave Courbet is about as explicit as you can get. Some people love it because it's so realistic and has a hairy bush, something you don't see a lot in Western art. But some people hate it because it's so depersonalized – the model has been decapitated: she has no face, no arms, no legs and consequently, no agency. She's basically been reduced to a vulva. Lesbian African-American painter Mickalene Thomas took Courbet's version and reimagined it as a self-portrait, making *Origin of the Universe* (2012). The work subverted this removal of power and gave back agency to the woman in the painting.

The V has a history of oppression, and reclaiming the V through art can be formidable. Between 2006 and 2011, non-binary South African artist Zanele Muholi created a series of works using their menstrual blood called *Isilumo siyaluma*, which is Zulu for period pains. Muholi writes,

my menstrual blood is used as a vehicle and medium to begin to express and bridge the pain and loss I feel as I hear and become witness to the pain of "curative rapes" that many of the girls and women in my Black lesbian community bleed from their vaginas and their minds.

The history of the V can be painful, and art is one of the most powerful ways to speak to it.

Where is all the pubic hair?

Particularly in Western art, there's a severe lack
of pubic hair. In Classical sculptures, it's
possible that the hair was painted on, and so by
the time it came to the Renaissance (a time
when artists were super into copying the ancient
Greeks), any paint that might have been there
wouldn't have survived for them to see. A bald
vulva represents youth and a lack of sexual
agency, ideals that they revered in women at the
time – which is super gross, when you think
about how sexualized the paintings were. In lots
of Arabic art around the same time, there also
wasn't hair, but that's probably because the
fashion was to shave. In Western art, a huge
turn came with Francisco Goya's *La Maja
Desnuda* (1797). Until then, women with pubic
hair in paintings were usually evil, sinners or
sex workers. But in Goya's painting, she is
confident and sexual, and the painting refuses
shame. Since then, pubic hair has turned up in
droves in Western art. If you want a pubic-hair
fix, I highly recommend Japanese art, especially
shunga, where there is pubic hair galore.

The backlash

In 2013, Casey Jenkins performed *Casting Off My Womb,* and it quickly went viral. For 28 days, she sat on a wooden box in a gallery in Australia and knitted a scarf. White wool was inserted into her vagina while she knitted, and the time she sat corresponded to one menstrual cycle – yes, there is a section of the very long scarf that is red. She says of the piece: 'It was a long, slow meditation on the intimate understanding we have of our own bodies and creative potential and how it's impacted by societal stereotypes and expectations.' A video of the piece spread like wildfire on the internet, and of course there was a huge backlash – mostly people displaying disgust. Jenkins believes that this came not from the fact that she was putting herself forward, but because she was doing it without shame. V art has often been controversial, and it really tells us something about how modern society views vulvas.

Renee Cox is a Jamaican-American artist who uses nude photography to 'celebrate Black womanhood and criticize a society she often views as racist and sexist'. A particularly controversial piece was *Yo Mama's Last Supper* (1996), a recreation of Da Vinci's *Last Supper.* Jesus was portrayed by the artist, who is nude with vulva on full display, and the disciples were all Black men (clothed) – except for Judas, who was a white man.

It speaks to how Black people have been betrayed, oppressed and killed by white supremacy. It was so controversial that when it was displayed at the Brooklyn Museum, the New York mayor at the time, Rudy Giuliani, called for museums to be subject to decency standards to prevent similar works from being shown. He exploited the confident display of the artist's vulva as a smokescreen to control the creative expression of Black women.

Contrast this to *Aktionshose: Genitalpanik* ('Action Pants: Genital Panic'), a series of six posters from Austrian artist VALIE EXPORT, born of a performance art piece. During the performance in an art film-house in Munich, she walked through the audience in crotchless trousers, exposing her genitals to their faces and holding a gun to their heads. In film, typically, the viewer and editor control the experience and thereby control the woman being viewed. But in this live performance, the woman who was being looked at controlled the experience instead. She subverted the male gaze by making the person being viewed an active participant, rather than a passive image on a screen. A photo of her in her crotchless trousers with a mop of wild hair, holding a machine gun, was taken in 1969 by Peter Hassmann. It's interesting to compare how this image of violence by a white woman generated much less controversy than an image of a Black woman posing as one of the most famous proponents of peace.

The most famous V art backlash was so strong it literally ended up in court. ろくでなし子 (Rokudenashiko) is a Japanese artist who makes art about まんこ (manko) (this means pussy, and because it is the word she uses, it's the word I'll use when describing her art). In 2013, after making manko art for a few years, she decided to crowdfund and make a manko boat by using a 3D scan of her own. Her art until this point had been lifesize, and she wanted something bigger and more meaningful. The reward for donating over 3,000 yen was a downloadable file of the 3D scan of her manko, which you could use to make your own version with a 3D printer. On 12 July 2014, police came to her house and said that distributing the 3D scan violated obscenity laws and encouraged 'reckless sexual impulse'. They confiscated her art and then arrested her. She was in prison for seven days, during which time she received global public support and a petition for her release that received over 20,000 signatures. She was later released on appeal. She believes that this backlash to her work was because she removed the manko from the realm of male desire and into her realm of personal joy, through funny, unserious artworks. In Japan it's completely legal to sell sex toys such as fleshlights – so the problem with her work wasn't that it was a manko, but that it was a manko not for male pleasure.[50] She is now living quite happily in Ireland with her husband and son. They even invited the Tokyo police to their wedding.[51]

50 She wrote about this experience with the justice system in a manga and was arrested a SECOND TIME just for talking about what happened to her. She was in prison for four weeks.

51 They didn't attend. Boo.

A musical interlude

Flip your tape to the V side and look these songs up on your favourite platform for some V bops.

'PYNK', JANELLE MONÁE

Afro-futurist, gender-boundary-pusher and queer queen of my heart Janelle Monáe released vagina anthem 'Pynk' in 2018. It's about as vulva-focused as you can get.

The dancers in the video have labia pants, and actress Tessa Thompson is birthed from Monáe's legs – it's literally perfect.

'GOD IS A WOMAN', ARIANA GRANDE

This is a song all about how Ariana is so mind-blowing in the bedroom, it'll be a divine experience and you'll believe 'God is a woman'. The vulvic imagery really comes through in the surreal video: Grande lies naked in a pool of lavender, vulva-shaped paint, a pair of giant legs are spread in Rome's Pantheon and the singer literally fingers the earth.

'SHAVE 'EM DRY', MA RAINEY

This song was first sung by dirty blues singer Ma Rainey in 1924, and there have been many fantastic recordings since. Dirty blues was a genre of blues music about all sex. 'Shave 'Em Dry' is all about having penetrative sex without any of the foreplay – as in, not had a chance to get wet yet. The opening lyrics of the Lucille Bogan version are like nothing you've ever heard before. Literally go look it up now – you won't be disappointed.

'WAP', CARDI B FEAT. MEGAN THEE STALLION

This song had the most searched-for lyrics online in 2020 and for good reason. The vagina anthem caused such controversy! It was reviled by the right wing for being too explicit, and it was reviled by the left wing for being . . . too explicit. The old argument was trotted out that women being publicly sexual didn't further feminism because it played into patriarchal ideas of objectification. I'm firmly against this – a woman enjoying sex and demanding what she wants? Feminist AF.

'STRAIGHT OUTTA VAGINA', PUSSY RIOT

Russian protest band Pussy Riot have a number of political songs under their belt and are well-known for criticizing Russian dictator Vladimir Putin – and being thrown in prison for it. Their anthem 'Straight Outta Vagina' is all about the power of the pussy.

'SHEELA-NA-GIG', PJ HARVEY

This song is all about a woman who makes an advance on a guy, but the man is intimidated by her forwardness. No matter, she says, she'll find a man who can handle her – there are plenty of men out there. And the title of course comes from our favourite exhibitionist church dwellers.

What do we want? Vs! How do we want them? In art!

Because the V is such an inherently influential body part, it's often used to make wider statements about feminism, women's rights and life in general. V activism takes so many forms, and I hope some of these examples might serve as inspiration.

Too long has the vulva been hidden away. Carolee Schneemann knew this when she performed her *Interior Scroll* in 1975, and it's considered a fundamental in feminist performance art. She came into the room fully clothed, undressed and wrapped herself in a sheet. She put on an apron and applied paint on her body. Finally, she pulled a scroll of paper from her vagina and started reading from it. At the first performance, the text on the scroll was an excerpt of her book *Cézanne, She was a Great Painter*. The second time it was performed in 1977, the text was an excerpt from her film *Kitch's Last Meal*, the text about a film critic who refused to watch her work. She explained she made the piece to 'physicalize the invisible, marginalized and deeply suppressed history of the vulva'. By taking an exploration of the world, relationships and the real actions of the patriarchy from inside her vagina, she made the interior exterior, forcing the audience to see what they refused to see – the vagina and its truth.

Judy Chicago's 1979 work, *The Dinner Party*, attempted the same, using the vulva as a jumping-off point to discuss women's history. The work comprises a triangular (read: vulvic) dinner table, with each place setting representing an important woman in history: from the ancients such as Ishtar to Hildegard of Bingen to modern civil rights leaders such as Susan B. Anthony. Each woman is represented by an artistic vulva on a dinner plate. Underneath the table are tiles with the names of a further 998 women[52] who hold an important place in history. It's now very famous, but when it was made it was derided by critics as 'kitsch'. It has since been the subject of more serious criticism. For example, the piece only has one place setting for a Black woman – civil rights leader Sojourner Truth, and though the plates become more and more abstract the further forward in time you go, her place setting is not vulvic at all and is in fact made up of three faces – a choice that Black scholar Hortense J. Spillers described as denying Black women their sexuality. Regardless, the work is considered a key moment in feminist art.

Smashing the patriarchy is something we should all strive to do, and Japanese artist Shigeko Kubota took this to a new level. In 1965 she performed *Vagina Painting* at a New York festival. She lodged a paintbrush in her underwear and used it to create abstract art with red paint. Comparing it to the work of French artist Yves Klein illuminates how misogynistic the art world often is, as Klein is famous for painting by dragging live women covered in blue paint across a canvas. His work objectified women – he literally turned them into objects. Kubota showed that you can still make similar art, in style as well as controversy, without needing to treat women like playthings.

Still daring today

In October 2021, the Vienna Tourist Board opened an OnlyFans account.

A few months prior, the art museum the Albertina was suspended from TikTok for showing the art of Japanese

---

52 There were supposed to be 999 women, but one of them is Kresilas who they thought was an ancient Greek female sculptor, due to a mistake in Matilda Betham's 1804 biography of famous women, but is actually a man.

photographer 荒木 経惟 (Nobuyoshi Araki), whose work often includes nudes. And not long after, the Leopold Museum had a post flagged as 'pornographic', even though it was the 1914 illustration *Liebespaar* ('Lovers') by artist Koloman Moser, which shows two nude people simply in an embrace.[53] In 2018, advertising regulators in Germany, the UK and the US refused to allow a tourism ad that included the nudes of Egon Schiele. The tourist board decided to resubmit the ads, but with a white censorship bar across the genitals and breasts with the slogan 'SORRY, 100 years old but still too daring today'. And herein, the museums of Austria saw an opportunity.

Vienna decided that enough was enough. The censorship of art could continue no more. So, they decided to upload their work on OnlyFans, where they could display it in all its glory. OnlyFans is a subscription website, where you can pay to see content of your favourite creators without ads. Without the ads, the platform is able to host sexually suggestive or explicit content that would usually be banned elsewhere. The move made news worldwide, and while the subsequent protest has come to an end, you can view all their posts on the platform for free now.

Vulvas are everywhere!

Erasing the vulva from art is a huge problem. It not only removes it from view, but it also makes it seem like it was never there in the first place. But now you know the truth – vulva art is everywhere. The vulva reigns all over the world as a symbol of power, pride and pleasure. It had long been a shame-free body part, so there's no reason we can't continue that today. So, feel loud and proud about your vulva, cast away any shame and celebrate your body as countless artists have before for thousands of years: **your body is a work of art**.

53 Not only is the vulva weirdly absent in this piece, she doesn't even have legs – just like a block of flesh?!

Chapter 7
VAGINA IS NOT A BAD WORD

I don't know who needs to hear this but . . .

. . . vagina is not a rude word.

You're a few chapters in now, but I want you to take a moment to reflect. When you read the word for the first time in this book, how did you feel? Disgusted? Relieved? Horrified? Elated? Baffled?

For so long, the language we use for the V has been considered rude and off limits, and it's time to change that.

When the Vagina Museum was registering as a charity in 2018–19 with Britain's regulatory body, the Charity Commission, the online form had a box for the charity's name. I, of course, typed in 'Vagina Museum'. The website served up the following error:

> **This name contains a word or words in the Charity Commission's banned words list.**

Yep. Vagina – the scientific name for a body part that 50 per cent of the human population has – is a 'banned word'.[54]

We argued that using this word was imperative – one of our charitable objectives is to educate the public about the V, and therefore we must use the scientific terms. The Charity Commission said 'public perception of the name may discourage

---

54 I mean, I'm assuming it's not the word 'museum'. That would be weird.

serious engagement'. They genuinely thought that using the word vagina would make people think badly of us. This is exactly why we need the museum to exist!

They asked: 'Will this name be found offensive?'[55]

NEITHER VAGINAS, NOR THE WORD TO DESCRIBE THEM, ARE OFFENSIVE.

So, being the keeno I am, I replied with a four-page essay making such points as:

- The word vagina is taught at school during biology. Therefore, it's not the name that may be found offensive, it's what the word represents that you're worried about.

- 65 per cent of women aged 16–24 in the UK say they have a problem using the words vagina or vulva.

- 48 per cent of girls aged 14–21 in the UK are embarrassed by their periods.

- 26.7 per cent of women aged 25–29 in Britain are too embarrassed to attend cervical screenings.

- In the past, you've registered charities such as testicular cancer charity The Oddballs Foundation, and if that's not considered offensive, why is our name, which is much less playful?

And most importantly: **how can we fight stigma if we can't name the stigmatized topic?**

Words are powerful. Language doesn't just reflect how we think, but it can in fact *shape* the way we think too. For example, in the first chapter I told you about how in Russian there are two separate words for blue: light blue/голубой and dark blue/синий. A study showed that Russian speakers are

---

55 I have no hard feelings against the Charity Commission and believe they were just doing their due diligence. After all, they approved the name in the end!

10 per cent faster at distinguishing shades of blue than English speakers. Having a word for something makes you better at understanding it, and – on the other side of the coin – not naming something makes it harder to think about and understand.

That's why using nicknames can be problematic, because it furthers the idea that vulvas are offensive, shameful and cannot be named. Using the correct words shows there's nothing to be afraid of and makes the V easier to understand and discuss.

If you want to love your V, you have to name it.

Why calling the vulva the 'vagina' is problematic

I'm probably not the poster girl for using the word vagina in the correct context. After all, I built the Vagina Museum, and it's about parts that aren't just the vagina! About twelve million people have asked me, 'Why isn't it called the Vulva Museum?' I was asked it so much that it's now the first question in our website's FAQs. But what's the alternative? The 'Gynaecological Anatomy Museum' doesn't sound like a fun place to go. Using words people recognize is important or they'll never walk through the door in the first place! Once you're inside, there's a display showing the correct words for all the parts, and in our exhibitions we **always** use correct terminology.

So why is it so important to use the right words? As we explored in the first chapter, not knowing the right words can make going to the doctor tricky and confusing.

It can also impact our sexual experiences. During sex, only 18 per cent of people with vaginas can orgasm from penetration alone. If it's not the main thing giving us pleasure (big up, clitoris), why are we focusing so much on it? Because it's the part the penis goes into. Calling the vulva the 'vagina' is cis-heteronormative. In other words, if we only speak about the vagina in relation to sex, we are implying that penis-in-vagina sex is the only valid experience, and we are prioritizing the pleasure of the person with the penis instead of the person with the clitoris.

But it's important to remember that not everyone's there yet. Language evolves, and right now 'vagina' is a common way to describe the vulva. Whether you agree this is good or not, it's happening. Using technically incorrect words happens all the time – just look at the word 'gut'. It means intestines, but it's commonly used to mean belly or the lower abdomen.

So use the correct words if you can, but don't shame anyone for using the wrong words. This is a shame-free zone! I'm just happy you're having the conversation at all.

**CALLING
A VULVA
A VULVA
IS ANOTHER
WAY OF
PRIORITIZING
OUR PLEASURE.
THAT'S PRETTY
DAMN
REVOLUTIONARY.**

Hollie McNish (she/her)
Writer

Vagina is not a bad word

I love playing with words. I've written poems since I was a teenager, and I'm now a professional poet. Recently, I've been scribbling a lot of poems about the words vulva and vagina, mainly because I find it so fascinating how difficult so many people, me included, find it to say these two tiny words – words that do not harm or insult anyone. We try and our whole body responds like 'ahhh, no, I can't, it's too weird!' Eleven letters, that's all – and we run from them as if fleeing fire.

It annoys me that I still have trouble pushing these two words out of my mouth and into the air. It annoys me because not only are the vulva and vagina just body parts, which half the population use daily, they are also personally two of the body parts that I've used the most and that have shown me nothing but love: from the very important ability to pee, to the physical pleasures of masturbation and loving sexual relationships, to the birth of my gorgeous daughter; these body parts have been very good to me, yet I still can't say their names without flinching.

Why? Why can I say words such as murder and hatred and gun, no problem. Or words that sound so similar, such as volcano, velvet and volvo, no problem.

When words, harmless as those words are, make us feel so strongly that we literally squirm about in our whole bodies when we try to say them, as if someone is asking us to lick a slug, I know they must be important. And they are!

vulva

. . . we compare it to a thousand fruits
flowers, figs and pomegranates
but still can't even name it

how absurd this bitter taste is
how can five split-second letters
rest so heavy on the tongue . . .

Firstly, they are parts of our body and we have a right to know what they're called. Also, if we're too embarrassed to say the words, then we're often too embarrassed to point out if they're sore or have a rash. We're unable to describe where we want to be touched, or how to find help if somebody touches us when we do not want them to.

When I was about 19, I didn't go to the doctor for years about a rash on my vulva because I literally didn't know how to describe where the rash was and I was too embarrassed to try. It led to three years of suffering. When I finally told the doctor I had a rash on my vulva, the left outer labia, I found out it was very treatable eczema, which was made worse by the rubbing of sanitary towels. I just wish I'd gone to the doctor sooner. When two of my close friends were teenagers, neither of them told anyone for years about sexual abuse they were suffering at home. They were too ashamed to talk. For both, this silence was partly aided by the shame they'd been made to feel about these body parts and the difficulty of feeling able to speak up without these words.

It is so, so vital to realise that they are not bad words or bad body parts. They are ours and are important, and nothing to be in any way embarrassed about. So many of us have been made to feel that way because of years of censorship, sexism and shaming. Argh! Many people just say vagina for everything because that's become normal, which is so confusing because it's wrong. They are two different body parts. We don't tell children that their arm is their shoulder just because we're too ashamed of saying the word arm. If a little boy said he was weeing from his testicles, I'm 100% certain he'd be corrected! Yet we let girls stay confused, ignorant and ashamed. I scribbled a quick poem.

saying vagina
when you mean vulva
is like saying throat
when you mean mouth

Some people say I overshare. Haven't I got anything better to write about? Yes, I do. I'd prefer to write about space travel to Mars and the fact that earthworms have five hearts, or the love I feel when I'm out dancing with friends. And I write about those things too. But until we're not ashamed to say these words, until we can confidently use them when we need to, I think I'll be scribbling about vulvas and vaginas for a while longer.

CALL A VULVA A VULVA

No definition found

In 2020, a journalist emailed me to comment on a story. In the official Scrabble app, Scrabble Go, you can search for words in the in-app dictionary to find the definition. The journalist discovered that the app did not provide definitions for a number of sexual, offensive and slang terms – one of which was vagina. At first, I was amused that someone was able to tell me a vagina fact I didn't know, and then so confused. Why allow you to play the word but not give the definition? Perhaps they were worried people would get too hot and bothered playing Scrabble . . .

This type of censorship is confusingly pointless. What's being achieved here? The word 'vagina' is a purely scientific name – it's what doctors and textbooks use. It is **not offensive**. There is a happy ending though. When this was brought to the attention of the app developers, they agreed to 'ensure all anatomical terminology will be properly defined in a future update of the game'. To check they kept their word, I downloaded the app and went to try to find it in the dictionary. Turns out you can only look up words that you have played, which meant I spent an embarrassing amount of time trying to get the right combination of letters to play the word 'vagina'.

These types of inconsistencies happen all the time, particularly on social media:

- When we were setting up the Vagina Museum's Facebook page, we weren't allowed to use 'vagina' in the handle (but for some reason we could put it in the page title).

- On TikTok, I tried to write a comment containing the word 'clitoris', but a pop-up told me it was 'against community guidelines'.

- For a while, searching #vagina on Instagram served up no results. This was finally corrected after a campaign headed by gynaecological cancer charity Eve Appeal, who give lifesaving information using hashtags with this word.

A lot of sex educators on online platforms have been finding creative ways to get around the censorship algorithms, such as replacing the word sex with 'seggs' or using emojis as word replacements. One of my faves is 'le dollar beans', which means lesbians. It started off as 'le$beans' to get around the censors, and it evolved from there. It only works until the moderators catch on before a new method emerges. And on and on it goes.[56]

56 At least the censorship is more targeted than it used to be. In the early days of the internet, people from Scunthorpe had a tough time talking about where they lived online. I'll let you figure that one out on your own.

I think the pointless and inconsistent censorship comes from the discomfort that people feel when they say or hear these words. Everyone knows what a vagina is – they are mentioned all the time in all sorts of contexts, from healthcare and culture to sex and family planning. Yet so many of us find it difficult to say the word aloud, and people go to great lengths to talk about vaginas without actually saying the word.

So, I've taken it upon myself to keep posting right through the censorship. I'll continue to post these non-offensive, important and valuable words and fight back whenever I'm censored. If you're reading this, come find me on social media – let's fight back together!

If it looks like a vulva and smells like a vulva . . .

Then why don't we call it a vulva? A euphemism is a word that replaces another that we consider too inappropriate to talk about directly – like saying you're going to powder your nose, instead of going to pee. But why do we do this for vulva or vagina?

Lots of people are too embarassed to say the word. Perhaps it makes them uncomfortable and using euphemsims make it easier to talk about. Or perhaps they think it's not an appropriate word to use.

You probably grew up calling your vulva a pet name, if you called it anything at all. A 2019 UK survey found 44 per cent of parents regularly use euphemisms to talk about vulvas; roughly 20 per cent of them never refer to their child's vulva at all, and only 1 per cent used the correct word. When I was a kid, my sister and I called ours either 'nunni' or 'front bottom', and across the world there seems to be a pattern to the slang we use as children. In English we've got foofoo, nuni, minnie, woowoo and hooha (among others). In Tagalog, there's *kiki*, and Spanish has *el chichi*. Basically, put a bunch of repeating sounds in a nonsense order and you've got yourself a child's nickname for a vulva.

And don't get me wrong, I understand why people do it – it's weird to hear the word 'vulva' come out of a toddler's mouth, just as much as I would be weirded out if a three-year-old said 'tax incentive' or 'laminate flooring'. And we use silly words around kids all the time for other things, so it makes sense to do the same with genitals. (Although personally I'm a big supporter of just using the correct anatomical words from the get-go.)

Slang turns up in our language for all sorts of valid reasons. It's used to form communities by having words you only know if you're 'in' the crowd. For example, for hundreds of years until the 1960s, the gay community, as well as people who worked in entertainment, the sex industry and the criminal underworld, had a whole set of slang words – verging on a secret dialect – called 'Polari'. Polari was a mix of words from Romani, Cockney Rhyming Slang, Romance languages, Yiddish and existing slang. It was useful because it meant people could talk freely without worrying about persecution or violence from the people around them.

Slang can also help convey the right tone for a situation and convey your attitude. If you're getting intimate with someone, how different would you feel if they used the word 'front bottom' compared to 'pussy'?

Slang is also important for understanding society's attitudes to vulvas. There are far more slang terms for vagina than there are for penis. In fact, there are probably hundreds – if not thousands – of slang words for vulvas and vaginas, and similar themes pop up all over the world.

Nature

- Lady garden or flower in English
- *Kehokeho* (hilltop) in Māori
- *Concha* (shell) in Argentine/Uruguayan Spanish
- *Cascata* (waterfall) in Portuguese

Animals

- Pussy in English, and also *chatte* in French, *muschi* in German, *poes* in Dutch and Afrikaans, and *mirri* in Finnish[57]
- *Mus* (mouse) in Swedish
- *Conejo* (rabbit) in Spanish
- *Păsărică* (small bird) in Romanian
- Beaver in American English
- *Aranha* (spider) in Brazilian Portuguese

Food

- Clam, tuna pocket, honeypot and beef taco in English
- *Fica* (fig) and *patata* (potato) in Italian
- *Cajeta* (a caramel sauce) in Argentine Spanish
- *Pruim* (plum) in Dutch
- *Panocha* (a type of sugar) in Mexican Spanish
- *Abricot* (apricot) in French
- *Žemlja* (a very vulvic-looking bread roll) in Slovenian

57 Although it's possible the English 'pussy' didn't actually derive from the word for cat, and instead could have been derived from an old Germanic or Norse word for 'pocket': pūss. And people noticed it sounded the same as the feline, and the words converged.

Depersonalizing words

- Downstairs or private parts in English
- あそこ (that place over there) in Japanese
- *Siri* (secret/private parts) in Swahili

Implied absence or negative space

- Hole or twat (which comes from an old word 'to twatch', which means to mend a gap in a hedge) in English
- *Zanja* (ditch) in Honduran/Nicaraguan Spanish
- Ծակ (hole) in Armenian
- فَرْج (opening) in Arabic

Violence

- Gash and axe wound in English
- *Snee* (cut) in Dutch

Literal

- *Pizda*, which turns up in various Slavic languages such as Russian, Ukrainian, Serbo-Croatian, Polish, Czech and Slovak, and actually derives from the Proto-Indo-European[58] *pisdeh*. It literally meant 'the thing you sit on'. A very rude word!
- 屄 (hai) in Mandarin, which literally means 'a hole in the bottom of your body' – again very rude
- *Tissekone* in Danish, which literally means pee-woman

Slang can be fun – I'm not saying we shouldn't use it. It adds a beautiful colour to our language and adds nuance that you

---

58 Proto-Indo-European is a hypothesized language that was spoken around 4,500–6,500 years ago. It is the origin of all languages spoken around Europe and Asia.

wouldn't get if you just spoke like a medical textbook. The use of slang is probably as old as language itself, which says something about its value. But it's important to have the correct words in our vocabulary too. It makes having serious conversations about health, puberty and relationships much easier and more effective. If something hurts, you need to be able to explain where. If someone touched you inappropriately, you need to be able to say exactly what happened. If we only use euphemisms and slang words – even when talking about serious things – it can lead to someone being ignored, belittled, embarrassed or even taken advantage of.

If we only ever hear our genitals being talked about with indirect terms as we are growing up, it teaches us that it's a part of the body that we should be ashamed of and forever hide away. And once shame sets in, it's so difficult to get out.

So absolutely do feel free to use slang – it's fun and I use it all the time! But know that there is a time and a place for it, and be confident using the correct terms when you need to.

And of course, a discussion about vulval slang would not be complete without . . .

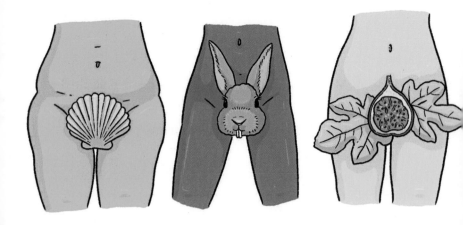

CUNT!

In 2004, the British Library commissioned a series of 26 artworks – one for each letter of the alphabet. Designers Morag Myerscough and Charlotte Rawlins got the letter C and designed a fabulous neon work that read: 'Has anybody seen Mike Hunt?' It caused an absolute ruckus, generating very angry newspaper headlines. And the word they were so angry about didn't even appear in the artwork.[59]

The word 'cunt' is generally agreed to be very offensive in the UK, beyond the pale in the US but neutral or even endearing in Scotland, Australia and New Zealand. And yet it's the oldest word in the English language for the vulva. It may even be the oldest in the whole world – tied with योनि yoni in Sanskrit. And while the word 'cunt' has been around for thousands of years, it's only in the last few hundred that it has been found offensive.

This word is like a microcosm for all the things I want to say about the vulva. People think it's rude, but there's no reason for it to be, and it hasn't always been this way.

Its etymology is very much up for debate:

- It could be Germanic, from the Old Norse *kunta*, which means the same thing.

- It's unlikely but it could be from Sanskrit – there's a character in the ancient Indian epic महाभारतम् (Mahābhārata), which was written somewhere between the third century BCE and the third century CE, called कुन्ती (Kunti). Kunti is considered to be an archetypal ideal woman.

- It's possible it came from Latin, in which the vulva is called cunnus.

In English, its first recorded use is actually in a street name

59 Say the sentence out loud to hear the pun.

from the 13th century – Gropecunt Lane. There are Gropecunt Lanes up and down the country,[60] and it's thought the name was used to advertise where sex workers worked. What this tells us is the word would have been in very common usage – otherwise it wouldn't have been a very effective advert!

In medieval times, the word 'cunt' was simply what the vulva was called. For example, in *Science of Chirurgie*, a 14th-century surgical textbook, the word 'cunte' is treated completely academically. We don't start to see the word 'cunt' being used in a slightly negative way until the end of the 1400s.

By the 1700s, the word seems to become really offensive. For example, it turns up in Francis Grose's *Classical Dictionary of the Vulgar Tongue* – a dictionary of slang words first published in 1785. He provides the definition of 'C**T' as 'a nasty name for a nasty thing'. Grose finds the word so unspeakable he has to asterisk it, which he doesn't do for the other words.

It isn't until 1860 that it starts being used as a disparaging word for a man. The word became so rude that despite it being over 700 years old, the *Oxford English Dictionary* – the definitive source for all words English – couldn't even bring itself to include the word until 1972.

Despite recent history declaring 'cunt' an offensive word, it's probably been a neutral word for far, far longer.

I think it's time we reclaim it.

And that reclamation is already in progress. In *The Vagina Monologues*, the pioneering play all about people's relationship with their V, there's a piece devoted to how wonderful the word is. It's repeated over and over, and the piece really lingers on all the letters.

But not everyone feels the same way. In a 1997 UK survey,

60 Many of these streets have been renamed 'Grape Lane' in the past few hundred years for the people who couldn't bear putting it on their letterheads.

'cunt' was ranked by respondents as the most offensive word there is.[61] It makes sense why other rude words are considered rude, as they're often racist or ableist. But this one means VULVA. If a word to describe our vulvas is considered the rudest, most offensive word ever, what does this say about our perception of this body part? Well, it suggests there's something shameful or vulgar about our bodies . . . which there most definitely is not.

This shift in the way society views the word 'cunt' is a phenomenon that happens over and over in language. It's called the 'semantic derogation' of terms for women, whereby over time the words that are associated with women often accumulate negative connotations.[62]

This has happened countless times throughout history. For example, a 'hussey' in the 1500s–1700s was the name for a housewife. Now, 'hussy' is used as an insult for a woman who has lots of sex. You can also see this happening when you look at gendered words that mean the same thing for men and women. Compare the images that come to mind when you think of a 'bachelor' compared to a 'spinster'. A bachelor is usually a sexy single man of any age enjoying his freedom, whereas a spinster is an old pitiful woman who is surely living a miserable life. This is despite the fact that the two words mean the exact same thing: a person who isn't married.

I want to end this conversation with one last thought, which comes from the perennially scandalous novel *Lady Chatterley's Lover* by D. H. Lawrence. It was published in 1928 and is about an upper-class woman who has an affair with one of her staff. The book is very sexually explicit, and the powers that be made any publication cut out all the naughty parts. In

61 The n-word was only ranked the fifth most offensive, which I think might say more about people in Britain than vulvas.

62 Just to reiterate – not all women have vulvas and not all people with vulvas are women. But society has created this link, which is why I use 'women' in this context.

the 1960s, Penguin (the same people who are publishing this book!) wanted to publish an uncensored edition in Britain, so it had to go to trial. Thankfully, the jury ruled in the book's favour, and we've been able to read about their sexy exploits totally legally ever since. In the book, Lady Chatterley asks her lover, Oliver Mellors, 'What is cunt?' after hearing the word and not knowing what it meant. And he replies:

'Cunt! Eh, that's the beauty o' thee, lass!'

THAT'S THE BEAUTY OF THEE.

C(o)untry matters

William Shakespeare is probably the most famous playwright in the world, but did you know about all the sex jokes in his plays? Hamlet – one of his most serious and tragic plays – contains what is likely to be the most famous cunt joke in all of English literature. Yes, really. In Act 3, Scene 2, Hamlet plays games with his paramour, poor Ophelia, where they have the following exchange:

HAMLET: Lady, shall I lie in your lap?
[Lying down at Ophelia's feet]

OPHELIA: No, my lord.

HAMLET: I mean, my head upon your lap?
[omg Hamlet, learn to listen to women when they say no]

OPHELIA: Ay, my lord.

HAMLET: Do you think I meant country matters?
[i.e. matters of the cunt. He means sex]

OPHELIA: I think nothing, my lord.

HAMLET: That's a fair thought to lie between maids' legs.

OPHELIA: What is, my lord?

HAMLET: Nothing.
[Nothing – between a maid's legs? Yep, it's Elizabethan slang for vulva]

OPHELIA: You are merry, my lord.
[merry means 'bawdy']

Shame, for shame

It's not just slang words that imply the vulva is something to be ashamed of. Many of the proper anatomical words we have for vulval-related parts literally derive from the word 'shame'. Sometimes, the patriarchy is explicit like that. It doesn't beat around the bush *(badum tssh!)*.

- *Pudendum* is an old-fashioned English word for external genitals – is derived from the Latin word *pudenda*, which means 'a thing you should be ashamed of'.

- *Srom* is Polish for vulva, but is derived from an old word for shame: *sromota*.

- The Indonesian word *kemaluan* means genitals, but also 'a shameful thing'.

The labia get it really bad. In many languages, the proper biological term that doctors use can be translated literally as 'shame lips'. For example:

Dutch	**schaamlippen**
German	**Schamlippen**
Norwegian	**skamleppe**
Danish	**skamlæbe**
Finnish	**häpyhuulet**

But it's getting better as lots of people have come round to the idea that your doctor calling your labia shameful is probably not great. For example, in Norway they are using *kjønnsleppe* more, which is along the lines of 'sex/gender lips'. This is similar to the Dutch *kønslæber*, and in German *Venuslippen* is being used more.

A similar initiative is happening in English. Doctors in the US are campaigning against having 'pudendum' and related words such as 'pudendal nerves' in the *Terminologia Anatomica* (the international medical dictionary). They were partially successful, as it was agreed they would replace pudendae with pudendales, which is a more grammatically gender-neutral way of saying the same thing. They've addressed the sexism problem within the term, but haven't quite got to the shame part yet. One step at a time, I guess.[63]

All around the world, the words we use instil a sense of shame about our bodies. It's important to be aware of the origins and meanings of words so that we can make informed decisions about how we use the powerful tool that is language.

Writing the clitionary

I've done a bit of digging on where some common scientific V words come from and what they really mean so we all have a better understanding of their origins. I, for one, know I don't want to be using words that once meant 'shame' for a part that I firmly believe is not shameful . . .

Vagina

The first recorded use of 'vagina' in English was in 1612 in a midwifery and paediatrics manual. The exact word 'vagina' is the same in other languages, including Latvian and Portuguese, as they all have the same Latin root. It comes from 'sheath' in a bunch of languages. A 'sheath' is a cover for a sword – which would make the penis the weapon and the vagina the place it lives. The sheath motif also pops up in Norweigan (*skjede*),

---

63 It wasn't easy though. It was such a controversial debate that people resigned over it, and they had to ban conversations about it for two years because tempers ran so high. All over an old Latin word.

Danish (*skede*), Dutch (schede), German (*Scheide*), Yiddish (שייד), Hebrew (נְרְתִּיק), Hungarian (*hüvely*), Icelandic (*slíður*), Lithuanian (*makštis*), Welsh (*gwain*) and Irish (*faighin*).

Vulva

'Vulva' first turns up in English around 1425 in a surgical and medical guide. You heard that right – the word vulva is older than the word vagina. Nowadays, the vulva refers to the external parts of the V and is a common word that appears in loads of languages, from Swedish to Romanian. Confusingly, the word vulva comes from the Latin for womb. It probably comes from the verb *volvō*, which means to wrap around or envelop, a likely reference to how wombs envelop foetuses inside. In ancient Rome and in many English texts until a few hundred years ago, they called the vulva *cunnus* – you can probably guess the equivalent word in English.

Clitoris

'Clitoris' was first mentioned in English in a 1615 anatomy textbook called *Mikrokosmographia* by Helkiah Crooke. For such an important part of the body, the clitoris (which is called the same thing in several languages including English, French, Mongolian and Thai) has a very uncertain etymology. It could be from the Hellenistic Greek for the same word, κλειτορίς (clitoris), but no one is sure where that came from. It could be from the ancient Greek κλείειν (*kleiein*), which means 'to shut', because it's often covered by the clitoral hood. I much prefer the suggestion that it comes from κλείς (*kleis*), which means a key – as the 'key' to pleasure is the clitoris.

Hebrew has a really interesting story when it comes to the clitoris. Hebrew stopped being used in everyday language around 200–400 CE, and was only used for prayer, legal documents and that sort of thing until it was revived in the late

1800s. Because of this long period of time where Hebrew wasn't spoken, there were loads of things that didn't appear in any surviving documents, so there just wasn't a word for them in Hebrew – and one of those words was 'clitoris'. In 1927, Naftali Herz Tur-Sinai published a German-Hebrew dictionary and needed to enter a word for clitoris. In German, to tickle is *kitzler*, which is also slang for clitoris. And in Arabic, tickle is دغدغة, or *daghdagha*, so he decided upon the word דגדגן or *dagdegan*. For a long time, the Academy of the Hebrew Language – a board of people who get to decide what goes in the dictionary – really resisted having a unique word for it, saying women apparently found it insulting. It was only in 2009 that they allowed dagdegan to be an accepted word.

Uterus and womb

The word uterus also turns up for the first time in *Mikrokosmographia*, and is Latin for womb or belly. For most of the book, Crooke calls it the 'womb', and only once is like 'oh yeah, it can also be called uterus'. So womb is probably the more common word historically and is also much older. Womb has a Germanic root and actually used to refer to the belly in general – so if you read texts from medieval times, there are loads of men who have wombs too. The womb also used to be called the 'matrix' (it's derived from the Latin for mother, which is *mater*), which I think is pretty cool. I like to imagine my womb in a black leather coat and sunglasses like Keanu Reeves.

What gender is a vagina?

In lots of languages around the world, nouns have a 'gender', and this even applies to inanimate objects.

In Russian, vagina is влагалище – pronounced *vla-ga-li-schye*. There are two interesting things about this word. First off, Russian has three grammatical genders – masculine, feminine and neuter. The gender of most Russian words is determined solely by spelling and not any perceived gender connotations. And *vlagalischye* is neuter! Living for the non-binary vaginas.

The second interesting thing is that the origin of the word is влагать – pronounced *vla-gat* – which means to 'put in' or to 'sheathe'. Yes, the sheath imagery persists.

In lots of other languages there is a link between spelling and gender (though there are many exceptions). This can lead to odd inconsistencies in the gender of certain words – for example, in French, vulvas are feminine (*la vulve*) and vaginas are masculine (*le vagin*). In Spanish, the uterus is masculine (*el útero*) but the vagina is feminine (*la vagina*). In Portuguese, cervix is feminine (*a cerviz*) whereas ovary is masculine (*o ovário*). All of which just goes to show that gender and sex perhaps aren't as linked as we once might have thought!

Lightning round

- *French:* cyprine is the vaginal fluid you make when you're aroused. How many languages have a word just for that?

- *Malay:* vagina in Malay is *faraj*. If you're aware of UK politicians, you'll know why this is funny.

- *Icelandic:* vagina is *leggöngum*, which literally translates as 'uterus corridor'. I love how utilitarian that is.

- *Cornish:* vagina is *kons* (unrelated to cunt) and means 'causeway', which results in *kons* meaning both vagina and pavement. Like Adele, I just keep chasing pavements.

- *Romani:* The word 'minge' is a loan word from the Romani word *mindž*.

A pocket guide for being a vagina-activist with your language

1. Use the correct terms for vagina and vulva whenever you can.

2. Avoid euphemisms in serious situations such as education and healthcare.

3. Say these words without any giggling or embarrassment.

4. Call out and call in people who use derogatory slang to refer to the vulva.

5. Call out and call in people who use slang words for the vulva as insults.

6. Be mindful to use gender-neutral language when referring to the V.

7. Remember that not everyone feels comfortable using the correct terms. As long as they aren't using offensive words, be understanding and lead by example by using the correct ones.

'Calling in' is when you compassionately inform people that they are doing something toxic because you want to keep them in your community, and 'calling out' would be ostracizing. Sometimes you do need to call out, though, when a person clearly doesn't want to change their behaviour.

What should we call the whole kit and caboodle?

When talking about the vagina, vulva and entire gynaecological anatomy, it's hard to know what exactly we should call it. Because so many of the options are gross, overly medical or have a history of violence, many people advocate for either a reclamation or creation of a new word entirely for the whole kit and caboodle.

'Gynaecological anatomy' is so clinical.

'Female reproductive system'? I have literally never used my bits for reproduction and only plan to maybe two or three times in my whole life, while some people may never use it for this purpose at all! Plus, the 'female' part is gender-exclusive. (I'll admit that 'gynae' derives from the Greek for woman – γυναίκα (gynaíka) – but how many of you knew that till I told you just now?[64])

What about **'sex organs'**? Not only does that make me feel like a slimy doctor from the 1950s, but again, there are plenty of things I use my vulva for that aren't sex. Or if by sex we mean those biological characteristics used to categorize us, we know already that this is an oversimplification as it's not so neat as vagina = female and penis = male.

And although **'vagina'** is commonly used to refer to the whole anatomy, we've already explored the problems with focusing too much on the vagina itself.

So what do we call it?

There's a huge wave of people who want to reclaim the word **'cunt'**, though this is very divisive considering the violence that has been associated with it. **Yoni**, or योनि, in Hindi, which originates in ancient Sanskrit, means both womb and vulva,

64 I mean, unless you speak Greek.

but I know that, as a white woman, saying it feels like major cultural appropriation.

Gloria Steinem suggested in the foreword to *The Vagina Monologues* that **'power bundle'** might be a replacement. It was decided by a group of teenage girls in a workshop she attended that it was their favourite phrase, and she thought to herself, 'What a long and blessed way from a hushed "down there"'.

Pussypedia, an online encyclopaedia about this body part, proposes **'pussy'** as a 'gender-and-organ-inclusive' word.

Sexologist Ann-Marlene Henning proposes **'vulvina'**, a blending of vulva and vagina as an entirely new word that has no negative historical connotations.

In Emma L. E. Rees's book *The Vagina: A Literary and Cultural History*, she ends with a call to arms to find this new name. She highlights her favourite contender: **'V'**, which was suggested to her by feminist academic Dr Lucy Ella. Not only does the letter V physically resemble a vulva, the shape also harks to the 'peace sign' we make with our index and middle fingers, or V for victory! The writer of *The Vagina Monologues*, who was previously known as Eve Ensler, has even renamed herself 'V' as a way of throwing off her father's name and releasing herself from his abuse. I love this new term so much – of course I do – I named this whole book after it!

For now, V is my favourite candidate for naming this part of the body, but that might change. Only time will tell if it catches on. It may be that with time, someone will propose an amazing replacement or one will just come naturally to the surface. All I know is that our vulvas, vaginas, uteruses, ovaries – this whole area of our bodies deserves a name that is as wonderful as the thing it denotes. A word with love, not violence. With joy, not shame. With clarity, not mystery. I hope one day we have a word that everyone can embrace.

Chapter 8
SMASHING THE BINARY

Vulvas, vulvas, vulvas. For every vulva out there, there's a unique relationship that goes with it. For a lot of people, their Vs and their bodies are a big part of their sex and gender. How you feel about yourself, your body and your identity is valid. If you feel like your V is a key part of your gender, that's cool. If your genitals have absolutely nothing to do with gender, that's also cool. If they are relevant but not key, then guess what . . . also cool.

Your body, your choice, after all.

How we as a society understand sex and gender has changed over time and varies around the world. There literally is no one correct answer to the question, 'What are sex and gender?' After all, if the answer was so simple, it wouldn't be so hotly debated. There are many ways to look at this question and many possible answers.

For much of Western history, sex and gender were seen as the same thing, and there were only two options – this is called the **sex/gender-binary**. The binary is where every person is put in one of two boxes, either:

Woman = XX chromosomes = vulva = kind-and-nurturing

or

Man = XY chromosomes = penis = strong-and-emotionless

While many people still agree with the sex/gender-binary, I don't. There are so many people who don't fit this framework, and when that many people don't fit a model, it's the model that's wrong, not the people.

For many years now, feminists have been teasing apart sex and gender. They have argued that sex is the biological bits (such as hormones, genes and genitals) and gender is the social bits (such as identity and roles and expression). But sex and gender are complicated concepts so even this is a massive oversimplification. The differences between sex and gender are not so clear cut and have been discussed by gender theorists for decades.

To lots of people, this topic is deeply personal, so it can get very emotional. When talking about sex, gender and people's identities, kindness and compassion is paramount. I'm endeavouring to write this chapter in a way that fully represents all the different experiences and understandings of gender in a sensitive way. And I hope you will join me in being kind and understanding.

What is sex?

In Western medicine, when a person is born, their sex is currently decided by observing their body – usually just the genitals – and assigning a sex category: male or female. You may have heard the terms 'assigned female at birth' (AFAB) or 'assigned male at birth' (AMAB), both of which refer to this moment where someone's sex is decided based on their genitals. But there are other biological sex attributes too:

- Gonads (usually ovaries or testicles)
- Chromosomes
- Genetics
- Hormones

And there are 'secondary sexual characteristics' as well, which appear during puberty, such as breasts and beards. Using these factors to put people into one of two boxes is called a sex-binary. The problem is, not everyone fits neatly into one of these two boxes (see 'What Is Intersex', page 24). Let's dig deep into **what sex actually is** and how it's way more complicated than just two neat boxes.

Chromosomes
How they work:

Chromosomes are packages of DNA within our cells. Humans have 46 chromosomes, arranged in 23 pairs, and each pair is formed from one chromosome from each parent. One of these is known as the sex chromosomes. Typically, people either have two X chromosomes (and are considered female) or an X and a Y chromosome (and are considered male). It's possible to have variations, though. Some people have just an X chromosome, have XXY or XXX – there are lots of potential combinations.

The X chromosome contains roughly 800 genes, but very few of them – quite possibly none, in fact – are involved in determining sex.[65] It is actually a gene on the Y chromosome called SRY that prompts the development of a penis.[66] Without it, our genes default to making a body with a vulva.

How it's not so simple:

The SRY gene is usually found on the Y chromosome. But it's possible for the SRY gene to migrate to an X chromosome. If that is the case, your body will make a penis and be stereotypically 'male' on the outside, but you'll have XX chromosomes. This is called XX Male Syndrome. So you see, a person can have the chromosomes that we typically consider female, yet have the genitals that we consider male. This shows us that it's not the chromosomes that are determining sex, and it must be the genes. We'll delve into them in a mo . . .

Often in arguments about sex and gender, people will say, 'But that's a very rare condition! Only 1 in 20,000 babies born have XX male syndrome. Let's not rewrite how we understand sex based on an exception!' But exceptions are important. Exceptions usually show that a model isn't working. Exceptions **challenge** rules.

Because here's the thing: what are these rules that our bodies are apparently trying to follow? Do you think a testicle whips out a biology textbook while making sperm cells to revise how to make them? No! It just does what it does without conscious thought because it's a *fricking testicle*. The idea that there are 'rules' our bodies should follow is something society decided.

And anyway, the idea that there are roughly 196,000 people around the world with XX Male Syndrome (if the stats

---

65 There's absolutely tonnes we still don't know about genes and what a lot of them even do.

66 This stands for 'sex determining region of the Y chromosome'. But I like to imagine it's the patriarchy saying 'SORRY'.

are right), yet they are considered an exception, is mind-boggling to me. That's so many people! If that many people are an exception, perhaps the current sex-determining system isn't that reliable.

Genes

How they work:

So, it appears it's not the chromosomes that determine sex but the genes. What are those genes? The big one to know about is SRY, which we just discussed.

How it's not so simple:

Having the SRY gene doesn't automatically lead to the male sex. For example, you can have the SRY gene and still develop a vulva. This can be due to androgen insensitivity syndrome (AIS), which is where the body is sort of 'immune' to testosterone. It's like the genes are going, 'Please make a penis!' but the body has its fingers in its ears, going, 'I can't hear you!'

This is really important to understand because we often use genes to determine legal sex. In the 1996 Olympics, female athletes underwent genetic testing to determine their sex and ensure that they were eligible to compete in women's sports.[67] Eight were found to have the SRY gene, which would have disqualified them from participating in the women's category. Fortunately, they were eventually allowed to compete, and a few years later, they stopped using genetic testing for sex verification. Many people are campaigning to remove this type of testing from sports altogether because it's so inaccurate. Sex is very complicated, and the tests don't reflect the natural diversity of humanity.

---

67 Weird how male athletes never have to have their sex verified (major side-eye).

Hormones

How they work:

A hormone is basically a chemical messenger that our body uses to deliver instructions. Hormones are really complicated, and can often deliver one message to one organ, and a totally different message to another. For example, serotonin is a hormone that affects your mood. But it's also involved in the gut and absorbing food, which means that serotonin abnormalities can lead to both depression and IBS.

The 'sex hormones' are a group of hormones usually categorized as 'male' (such as testosterone) and 'female' (such as progesterone and oestrogen).

How it's not so simple:

Here's the thing about sex hormones – BOTH ARE PRESENT IN EVERYONE'S BODIES![68] The hormones are used for many things other than sex-related matters. For example, oestrogen is also used to regulate cholesterol and maintain bone health IN EVERYONE. Oestrogen is made by the ovaries, but also by the adrenal glands and fat tissue. Testosterone is also by the adrenal glands, and guess what – THE OVARIES TOO![69] That's why **every single person** has both these hormones, regardless of sex – they are made in organs that aren't sex organs. By labelling them sex hormones, everything they do suddenly is sexual, even if it has nothing to do with sex. If we thought of oestrogen and testosterone as simply growth hormones, would we think of them as so intrinsic to sex?

There's also a lot of misconceptions about what sex hormones do. For example, there's a perception that more

---

68 The hormones are also extremely similar. The body makes oestrogen by making testosterone first and changing it slightly.

69 I know, I really need to calm down – it's just this is something I'm really passionate about.

testosterone makes a person bigger and stronger. Seven to 10 per cent of people with ovaries have PCOS, and a symptom is having higher-than-average testosterone levels. But they aren't all being pushed to compete as weightlifters! What has been shown to have a much greater effect is changes to your natural levels of these hormones, but it's definitely not as simple as lots of testosterone = big and strong.

Genitals and gonads

How they work:

This one should be pretty obvious. There are usually penises and testicles or vulvas and ovaries. They come in lots of shapes, sizes and variations.

How it's not so simple:

Prepare to have your mind blown. Did you know that penises and vulvas are basically the same organs, just arranged differently?

At the start of our lives, foetuses have the same body parts regardless of what genitals they'll eventually have. These 'proto-genitals' look much more like a vulva than a penis. If there is no SRY gene, it will continue developing into a vulva. At around nine weeks, if the SRY gene is present, the body will stop developing a vulva and make a penis instead. What would have been the clitoris gets larger to become a penis, what would have become an ovary becomes a testis and so on. A clitoris and a penis are basically the same organ, with the only major differences being size and whether the urethra goes through it or next to it.

FUN FACT: This is the cause of the penile raphe – the line on the underside of the scrotum and penis. During development, what would have been the labia majora get fused together to make the scrotum. The labia minora are fused together to make the skin on the penis. That line on the underside of the penis is a relic of this event.

Secondary sexual characteristics

How they work:

Secondary sexual characteristics are the names given to body features that appear during puberty, such as boobs, beards, chest hair, general hairiness, height, weight distribution, depth of voice, Adam's apples and pubic hair. Most of these are usually associated with one particular sex.

How it's not so simple:

Many of these characteristics **do not** wholly belong to one sex. Many cis women have moustaches.[70] Some people with PCOS can even grow full beards. People who are assigned male at birth all have breast tissue – their breasts are just usually flatter.

Lots of people who have a secondary sexual characteristic that doesn't 'match' with their sex face discrimination. Think about how men are shamed when they are short or have 'man boobs'. Or how women are considered unattractive if they have facial hair or if their shoulders are too wide. This shaming happens because they don't fit the socially constructed sex-binary.

---

70 My father tells me my grandmother would get rid of her moustache by lighting it on fire, which is pretty badass. But so I don't get sued – please don't try this at home.

Well then, what IS sex?

Sex has roughly five factors: chromosomes, genes, hormones, genitals and gonads, and secondary sexual characteristics (although some might argue there are more or less – this is just how many I would count). And it's **humans** who decide which factors are relevant. This means that any answers to the question 'what is sex?' are rooted in culture, not biology. That doesn't mean sex isn't real – it just makes understanding it a **cultural** exercise.

Every person lives somewhere on this wibbly-wobbly-multidimensional-culturally-defined scale of each of those factors, and yet we try to put all those people into only TWO categories. Let me give you a challenge: try to draw a five-dimensional cube on a two-dimensional piece of paper. Pretty difficult, huh? And yet that's what we try to do with sex.

If I had to sum up sex in two words, it would be this: it's complicated. It's why I love biology so much. When I was at secondary school, I had a running joke with my friend about science class. We would study hard all year, then go on summer holiday. And when we came back in September, our new science teacher would tell us, 'So everything you learnt last year was actually an oversimplification and maybe even a bit wrong because of how much it was simplified. Here's how it *really* works . . .' And this would happen year after year. We would joke 'everything we know is wrong!' And that planted a seed of existential dread I've never been able to shake.

The healthiest way to look at science (and life in general!) is to think, *'We don't know the full picture, we probably never will, but this is our best understanding of it right now and next year perhaps we'll learn something new that changes everything.'* So I'm sorry that I haven't given you some clear and well-defined answer of what sex is. All I can give you – all I can *ever* give you – is the **best understanding that we have right now**.

What I can tell you is that oversimplifying sex causes harm to real, living people. People who are intersex are sometimes labelled as 'abnormal', and their bodies are classified as a 'disorder'. But roughly the same proportion of people around the world have red hair. Red hair occurs due to a genetic mutation, but do we think that red hair is abnormal? That the only valid hair colours are blonde or brown/black and that red hair is an 'exception'? Or even a disorder? Of course not! So why do we think this about people with sex variations?

The sex-binary model is **flawed**. By understanding that it is a massive oversimplification, we can fight for a more inclusive definition that takes into account everyone's lived experiences.

Four intersex people from history you should know about

Karl M. Baer (1885–1956)

Karl M. Baer was born to a German-Jewish family and had ambiguous genitalia. There was some debate about whether to raise him as a boy or a girl. The doctor and father advocated for girl, whereas his mother for boy. She was overruled, and Karl underwent surgery. He grew up to be a suffragist, fighting for women's rights around Europe. He later transitioned and began living as a man, and in 1906 went to pioneering doctor Magnus Hirschfeld to become the first person in the modern world to undergo gender-affirming surgery. He published a memoir called *Memoirs of a Man's Maiden Years* in 1907 under the pen name N. O. Body.

Thomas/ine Hall (early 17th century)

Thomasine Hall was born in Newcastle, UK, around 1600 and was raised as a woman. In their mid-20s, he joined his brother in the English army as a man named Thomas. After leaving the army, she was a woman for a few years in England, then emigrated to Virginia, USA, as a man. After working in the US for a few years and sometimes living as a man, sometimes a woman, they were subjected to numerous violating inspections to determine whether they were a man or a woman. The legal system ruled in one instance that Thomas/ine was a man and in another a woman. In 1629, in an historic legal case, a judge ruled that they were both man and woman and legally bound them to wear both men and women's clothing at the same time. There are no further records after this date, and it's unclear if Thomas/ine ever found peace.

Witold Smętek (1910–1983)

Witold Smętek was an intersex Polish athlete assigned female at birth. He participated in a number of women's sports including javelin, shot-put, cross-country, cycling, table tennis and Czech handball. In 1936, he underwent gender-affirming surgery and lived the rest of his life as a man. He published a book about his experiences called *A Confession of Love of a Woman Who Became a Man.* During WWII, he was active in the Polish resistance to Nazi occupation. After the war, he worked as a history teacher and gave history tours of Warsaw.

Lê Văn Duyet (c. 1763–1832)

Văn Duyet was born in Định Tường province, Vietnam, to a family of farmers. Born with ambiguous genitalia, he was raised as a eunuch.[71] While fleeing a coup, Prince Nguyen Phúc Ánh (who later became Emperor Gia Long) spotted his intelligence and asked him to join his court. He joined the army and quickly rose through the ranks due to his talent for military strategy. He didn't get on well with the emperor's

successor, Emperor Minh Mang, as they vehemently disagreed on many issues. They fought until Duyet's death, to the point where the emperor desecrated Duyet's tomb. The emperor's son, upon his succession, restored it and it later became a national monument.

---

71 In Vietnam at the time, being a eunuch was a political/social position where people were castrated and allowed to have certain jobs.

What is gender?

How we understand gender has changed through time and varies across cultures. Gender doesn't exist in a vacuum – it's tied up in race, sexuality, religion, capitalism, class and more. For example, how womanhood or manhood is experienced will be different depending on if you are White, Black, Asian, Arab, Latina or another race. Or if you are working class or wealthy. Being non-binary or genderqueer will be experienced differently depending on the culture around you. This is intersectionality in a nutshell. Each person's experience of gender is unique because we all have a unique set of influences in our lives. This is why there is no one singular definition of what gender is.

What are some of the factors that make up gender?

As I mentioned, our understanding of gender varies from culture to culture. For example, take jewellery. In some cultures, jewellery is only for women. In other cultures, men and women wear jewellery. Or high heels – most people today would argue high heels are a women's fashion item, but in the 17th-century French court of Louis XIV, high heels were mostly worn by men and were a way of showing off wealth.[72]

It's highly debated whether certain things should be considered masculine or feminine, or whether something should be a factor of gender at all. For example, many believe – and I agree – that our gender shouldn't determine the type of work we do. The idea that women should care for the family and men should work for profit should absolutely be a gender factor left in the past.

72 You know what they say about men with large high heels ... more likely to get their heads chopped off by revolutionaries.

When society states that a certain gender must look, act and feel a certain way, this can become a harmful stereotype. I remember vividly being called 'unladylike' when I was young, for being loud and ungraceful. That hurt and confused me because I knew I was a girl, but according to some adults, I was apparently very bad at it. Many men have the same problems – for example, if they show any emotion that isn't stereotypically 'masculine', they might get called a 'sissy'. We're so often expected to 'pick a side' in order to fit in, but no one should be told how to do gender. Each person should be able to decide for themselves.

There are a few common themes that pop up a lot in conversations about gender:

Roles

This can be anything: from the types of labour we do, to our roles in the family and wider society, to how we act in relationships. For example, the belief that women should care for the home and family but men make the big family decisions.

Norms

How society thinks a gender should act and feel. For example, some cultures believe that women should be nurturing and emotional and men strong and stoic.

Identity

How a person feels internally about their gender.

Experience

The intersection between identity and norms. In other words, thinking about the way a person feels about themselves and whether it matches up with how society views and treats them. It can make someone feel like they belong or it can make them feel uncomfortable, unhappy or unsafe.

Expression

How a person expresses their gender, such as through clothes, hairstyles, body language or how their voice sounds. Not everyone can express their gender in the way they want to for fear of violence and discrimination.

So now to add to the multidimensional cube of sex, we also have a multidimensional cube of gender. I'm starting to think the human experience might be difficult to define . . .

Do sex and gender interact?

The idea that sex and gender live in two separate spheres is an oversimplification. Sex and gender in our modern society absolutely interact, in the same way that they interact and intersect with our race, class, age and other facets of our identity.

A person's sex can influence the gendered expectations they face. For example, people with penises are often encouraged to be strong, meaning that when they go to the gym, they may focus on weightlifting as opposed to flexibility. Over time, such gender expectations can literally affect your biology as you focus on different parts of your body.

Or take women's education. It was widely believed for a very long time that biologically, women were intellectually inferior to men. This belief justified women being treated as subordinate. Darwin came along and made matters even worse with the theory of evolution. He argued that males developed higher intelligence in order to attract more mates. But women at the time were literally being barred from education, so of course it would appear they were not as clever – apparently, we are supposed to just instinctively know Latin and quote Plato coming out of the womb. Feminists argued, '**Why not educate women, then decide on our intellectual abilities.**' So as you can see, sex and gender can't be so neatly divided into just sex = biology and gender = society. They interact way too much, and life is too complex for it to be so neat. If there is one thing we can take away from this, it's that we don't need to be defined by what society expects of us. Everyone should have the right to decide for themselves what they want out of life.

A new model

In the sex/gender-binary model, if you are assigned the female sex at birth, you are also assigned the female gender. And the same for male sex and male gender. In the modern, somewhat more inclusive model of sex = biology and gender = culture, sex and gender have been separated from one another. In this new model, any sex and any gender can go together.

Your gender can be the same your whole life or it can change over time. And that is perfectly valid. Also, sometimes people are unable to be open about their gender for fear of persecution and violence. Just because someone isn't open about their gender doesn't make it any less valid.

I want you to know that no matter what gender you are, you can have a V, love the V or be a V-activist. Your identity and experience are valid and no less important than anyone else's – and don't let anybody tell you otherwise.

Gender around the world

The many different genders

Here are some of the genders out there that you might have heard of. As our understanding of gender expands, so does the list.

- **Cisgender:** when your gender matches the gender you were assigned at birth.

- **Transgender:** when your gender doesn't match the one you were assigned at birth.

- **Non-binary:** an umbrella term for when your gender doesn't fall into the binary system of female or male.

- **Agender:** when you have no gender.

- **Genderqueer:** when your gender does not fit conventional gender norms.

- **Genderfluid:** when your gender is dynamic and not in a fixed static state.

- **Multigender:** an umbrella term for having more than one gender.

- **Bigender:** when you have two genders – they could be simultaneous or experienced at different times.

- **Trigender:** when you have three genders – they could be simultaneous or experienced at different times.

- **Demigender:** an umbrella term for when you have a partial connection to a gender, such as demigirl/demiwoman, demiboy/demiguy, deminonbinary or demifluid

- **Neutrois:** when your gender is neutral.

- **Gender non-conforming:** when your gender doesn't align with the traditional expression of that gender. Cis people can be also gender non-conforming – for example, masculine cis women or feminine cis men.

Having conversations about gender can be difficult if you've never done it before. A good rule of thumb is to use your instinct – is this a question you would ask a cisgender person or is it too personal or prying? 'What pronouns do you use?' – great question. 'What genitals do you have and have you ever had surgery on them?' – absolutely not, that's rude.

Culturally specific genders

The gender-binary does not exist everywhere, and many different cultures have different gender systems. While there is some difficulty describing cultural concepts not in the original language, I have done my best to accurately portray them. These genders are culturally specific so it's important not to appropriate them. Here is just a small selection:

Hijra/Khwaja Sara/Aravani, South Asia

Hijra people are people with penises or are intersex who take on a feminine appearance and are considered a third gender. They generally live in hijra communities and perform religious rituals and blessings at births and weddings. Whereas they were greatly respected in pre-colonial South Asian culture, they are now quite stigmatized as a result of British colonialism and missionary Christianity, which forced the sex/gender binary and heteronormativity on South Asian culture. It's estimated there are three million hijra living in India as of 2014.

Burrnesha (sworn virgins), Albania and Kosovo

Sworn virgins are people with vulvas who live as men. It developed out of a Kanun – a medieval legal decree that stopped women from voting, buying land or holding certain jobs, among other things. So some people with Vs promised not to marry or have children, and to live as men in order to have the same rights as cis men. There are very few burrneshas left.

Fa'afafine and Fa'afatama, Samoa

Fa'afafine literally means 'in the manner of women' and refers to people who are AMAB who live as women, non-binary or third gender. Fa'afatama means 'in the manner of men' and is the name for people who are AFAB who live as men, non-binary or third gender. They have traditionally been well respected and an important part of Samoan culture but since the advent of British colonialism, have experienced discrimination, marginalization and invisibility. In some families, the traditional recognition of fa'afafine and fa'afatama means that children are not discouraged from engaging in play or interests traditionally associated with other genders.

Two-spirit, Indigenous North American

Two-spirit is a gender category that was formalized at the 1990 Third Annual Native American Gay and Lesbian Gathering. It's an umbrella term for the many gender identities beyond 'female' and 'male' within more than 500 Indigenous North American cultures.

The five genders of the Bugis people, South Sulawesi, Indonesia

In the Bugis culture, there is a five-gender system: *makkunrai* (roughly comparable to cis women), *oroani* (~cis men), *calabai* (~trans women), *calalai* (~trans men) and *bissu* (~polygender, non-binary or intersex). None of these genders are considered equivalent and each perform different social roles.

Muxe, Zapotec cultures of Mexico

The Zapotec are an indigenous people of Mexico, and Muxe are people who are AMAB but don't act masculine. Muxe people are highly respected, often involved in ceremonies and caring for the family. To have a Muxe person as part of the family is generally considered a blessing.

Jay Hulme (he/him)
Writer and poet

Reclaiming manhood

As a trans man who passes as a cis man, I am often met with confusion when I tell people that I'm trans. They laugh awkwardly, their eyes go wide, they ask if I'm serious. My reply is always, 'Yeah, I'm a man with a vagina.'

There's something about that statement that makes them realize I'm not joking – after all, in a transphobic society, the idea of trans people is the punchline of so many jokes – but the lack of a penis? Somehow that's deadly serious.

That's because we live in a world that has wrongly believed that men are better than women for centuries, and in which there's a widespread belief that how much of a man you are is about how much of a penis you have. It's why people spend so much time googling average penis sizes. It's also why, when people politely try to avoid saying the word 'penis', they use the term 'manhood'. To be a man without a 'manhood'? For some people, it means you're no man at all.

That idea is wrong, but lots of people still think it. When I came out as trans, even more people thought it than they do now. The idea that you cannot be a man without a penis meant that I was constantly asked when I would get 'the surgery'. There are many surgeries trans men can have if they want, but what the people asking me that question meant was 'when are you getting a penis?'. I didn't know how to explain to them that getting a penis was at the bottom of my priority list. After all, there's so much more to my existence as a man than what is, or isn't, in my pants.

For many years, though, I struggled with this implication that I couldn't fully be a man without a penis. It was compounded by the widespread stigma around vaginas. After all, I had spent my whole life surrounded by jokes and insults that persuaded even cis women that their vaginas were dirty or ugly or somehow bad. Sadly, it took me a long time to realize that being a man with a vagina isn't a bad thing. That a person's personal manhood has nothing to do with the size, or even the existence, of the 'manhood' between their legs. That I had nothing to be ashamed of.

Funnily enough, it was feminist activism that helped me to fully understand myself as a man, and to see my vagina as a positive thing. The fight to remove the stigma around vaginas is still ongoing, but for me, inside my heart, that fight is won.

It may have taken years, but I know now that being confident in who I am, regardless of what others think or expect, is the final rejection of transphobia. It is also a rejection of the sexism that makes us think of vaginas as bad or lesser.

> **These days I move through the world as fully myself – a man, entire. A man who just happens to have a vagina. A man who is proud of that fact.**

Five gender non-conforming people from history you should know about

One of the most common transphobic arguments is that being trans is a modern 'fad' that shouldn't be taken seriously. So right now feels like the perfect opportunity to tell you about a few people from the past who show us how this is entirely false!

A quick caveat: we have to be very careful with calling people from the past 'trans' or any other label. Firstly, the term is quite modern, and we have no idea if that person would have identified with these labels had they lived today. Secondly, our ideas of sex and gender have massively evolved throughout time and around the world, so the words we use now are unlikely to fit the understanding of gender at the time when many of these people lived.

Nzinga, Queen of Ndongo and Matamba (c. 1583–1663)

Nzinga was queen of the Mbundu kingdoms in modern-day Angola. When she ascended the throne, Europe was invading Africa, enslaving people and forcing them to convert to Christianity. After a peace treaty with Portugal fell apart, she successfully held back Portuguese colonialist efforts until the end of her life. She often dressed as a man and had a harem of chibado[73] lovers.

Saint Marinos the Monk (c. fifth century)

Marinos was a monk in Syria, Lebanon or Turkey (sources differ) who was AFAB and a man. When he was falsely accused of impregnating a woman, rather than pointing out it was impossible, he took in the baby and cared for them. There is a Greek Orthodox church dedicated to him in Bristol, England.

Amelio Robles Ávila (1889–1984)

Amelio Robles Ávila was born in Xochipala, Mexico. He was AFAB, and in his early twenties transitioned to being a man and joined Zapatismo, a guerrilla army led by Emiliano Zapata in the early 1910s. He eventually rose to the rank of colonel, supporting a number of revolutionary leaders.

73 Chibado is a Ndongo third gender similar to trans women.

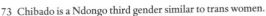

Public Universal Friend (1753–1819)

Public Universal Friend (PUF) was a Quaker preacher born in Rhode Island, USA. In October 1776, PUF fell gravely ill. After recovering, PUF said that PUF's previous soul (that of a woman) had ascended to heaven and in its place was a new genderless spirit charged with spreading the word of God. When people asked PUF what gender PUF was, PUF would simply reply 'I am that I am'. PUF asked people not to use pronouns for PUF.

We'wha (1849–1896)

We'wha was an ambassador of the Zuni people, in modern-day New Mexico, USA.

They were an lhamana – a type of two-spirit gender. We'wha was an exceptionally skilled crafter known for weaving and was also skilled in medicine and ritual dance. They travelled with anthropologist Matilda Coxe Stevenson and her  husband to Washington, D.C., in 1885 to share Zuni culture. This, however, did not prevent US authorities from continuing their oppression of lhamana people.

Gender liberation

What would happen if we lived in a world where there were no expectations or norms around how gender should be? Where your V didn't mean society required you to live and act in a certain way?

In our current society, sex and gender have, I think, a weird amount of precedence.[74] My sex is recorded on my passport, driving licence and tax documents.

Why does a border control agent need to know what's in my pants to decide if I can visit an art gallery and drink sangria?

Why do the police need to know my sex if they've pulled me over? Doesn't that feel weird?

Why does the government need to know what my genitals look like to know how much tax I should be paying?

If I wanted to change what it says on my documents, why does a doctor or judge need to approve it?

Why is it so important for the establishment to 'approve' my gender? Why is it any of their business? **Why is our society so obsessed with policing our sex and gender**? Oh actually, I think we all know why.

I want to fight for true gender liberation. And when I say we should have gender liberation, I don't mean all people should become genderless identical robots. What I mean is that **all people** deserve to live in a world where everyone can live and express gender without fear of violence, stigma or discrimination. Where we can explore and discover different parts of gender without cruelty or expectations forced upon us. A world where people can live in gender freedom.

---

74 It's important to note that this is not universal. There are many cultures where other factors are more important than gender, such as social rank or age.

GENDER LIBERATION FOR ALL!

Chapter 9

YOUR VULVA WILL NEVER SMELL LIKE A CANDLE

Have you ever walked down the feminine hygiene aisle at the supermarket and thought, *Is all this necessary? Do I really need to use all these products?* Well, my friend, these are *very* good questions.

We are constantly being told by society that our vaginas are dirty. Smelly. Messy. Disgusting. Bad. You've probably seen products for vaginal cleaning or 'yoni steaming' on Instagram. Maybe you've seen ads for vaginal deodorants, sprays, wipes, douches and who knows what else. And maybe you've started to wonder, why are these companies telling you that your natural body is gross? It's literally called 'the feminine hygiene industry', as though our vulvas are naturally unhygienic.

Why are we told all this? You know already that patriarchy is at work here, but there's another major factor at play. Money. Or more specifically, **capitalism**.[75]

The global 'feminine hygiene' market was valued at $19 billion in 2020. The more we are told our bodies are disgusting, the more shame we feel and the more products we buy. If you were happy and proud of your body, would you buy all of this rubbish? Almost certainly not. The industry is based on shame. But I'm here to tell you something radical: **There is absolutely nothing shameful about the way our vulvas naturally look or smell.**

Understanding that we live in a capitalist society that profits off making us ashamed of our bodies is revolutionary. It's a way of standing up for yourself and realizing your worth. I hope this chapter stays with you as you're walking through shopping aisles, watching adverts, learning from and listening to the people around you. I hope it stays ingrained in your mind as you wonder if you really need to buy a certain product that promises to make you more acceptable according to society's standards. I hope it helps you question – who is setting these standards?! By the end of this chapter, I hope you'll have the confidence to strut down the feminine hygiene aisle and shout:

I don't need you. I love myself as I am.

75 To be perfectly clear, capitalism is an economic system, where individuals (or a small group of individuals) own and run companies, and the profits flow to the person(s) at the top rather than the workers.

To be a V-activist is to be anti-capitalist. Capitalism doesn't want you to love your vulva. This system has one goal – profit. Everything in a capitalist society is motivated by profit, and that's why companies will do anything they can to sell us products, including shaming us. Constantly being told our bodies aren't good enough forces us to buy stuff to try and make our bodies meet society's expectations. And when society's expectations are entangled with these harmful messages of shame, we end up with pointless and often dangerous products that have ABSOLUTELY NO BENEFIT AT ALL. I could talk for days about the harmful impacts of capitalism and how it touches every part of our lives, from climate change to racism. It disproportionally affects women, people with Vs and people of marginalized genders. If we want to dismantle the patriarchy, we must also do the same to capitalism as they are too interconnected. WELCOME TO ANTI-CAPITALISM, MY FRIEND. I only have space to touch on this lightly in this book, but at the back of the book I hope you'll find the additional resources helpful if you'd like to read more.

Damaging myths are there to squeeze money from us

Steam, jade eggs, lighteners – all things that I would strongly recommend you keep far away from your V. Any company or person that makes money by telling you that your vagina is dirty and needs these products is not feminist.

It is with great regret that I find myself telling you about a 'treatment' called yoni steaming. There are some people around the world who do find it useful, but you should know about the serious risks involved. It involves squatting above boiling herby water, in order to 'cleanse your yoni' (the vagina and uterus). NEWSFLASH: your vagina and uterus categorically **do not** need cleaning. If they were 'dirty' in any way, you'd be seriously ill and likely to end up in a hospital with an infection. And if they were so dirty and in need of a clean, they certainly wouldn't be growing foetuses inside them!

Yoni steaming has got completely out of hand in recent years. Practitioners claim the treatment can cure anything from infertility and fibroids to low libido. (Which it absolutely doesn't – just in case you were wondering.)

Here's the main reason: **steam simply can't get into your uterus.**

1 The vagina is not a gaping hole for steam to go up – it sits closed.

2 The cervix has a tiny, tiny hole in it and steam just won't get through it, even if it manages to somehow get into your vagina in the first place.

Also, I hate to point out the obvious, but steam can seriously burn your vulva.

Many yoni-steaming practitioners claim that it's an 'ancient Korean treatment', but I have found absolutely no evidence of this. This claim is often based on highly offensive Orientalist beliefs. Orientalism is the fetishization of Asian and Arab cultures, and it is a type of racism. It is also a form of cultural appropriation (the misuse and misrepresentation of a culture, often for the sake of humour or profit). Goop did it with their jade yoni eggs as well, claiming they were a 'guarded secret of Chinese royalty'. Goop (a 'wellness and lifestyle brand' founded by actress Gwyneth Paltrow) was fined $145,000 in 2018 for making false claims about jade eggs, such as saying they could prevent prolapse and regulate your menstrual cycle.

So where did yoni steaming really originate? It used to be called 'womb fumigation' (no wonder they rebranded it!) and since ancient Greek times, it was believed in the West that the uterus was an independent being living inside our bodies, like 'an animal within an animal'. And it would get restless if it didn't have enough to do, causing all sorts of problems such as shortness of breath and even madness.[76] And so any time a woman went to the doctor with a problem, what was their diagnosis? The uterus must be in the wrong place! The first proposed solution was to get pregnant, as a foetus would weigh the uterus down and occupy it, preventing it from wandering idly. But if that wasn't available, there was another option. What's an animal's strongest sense? Smell, of course. The idea was to entice the womb to return to its home by putting nice smells near the right place. It's a practice that mostly disappeared by the 1700s, and I wish it had stayed there, rather than returning as the rebranded 'yoni steaming'.[77]

76 Madness caused by a wandering womb was called 'hysteria'. Υστέρᾱ, or hystera, is Greek for womb. Yes, the origin of that word is the medical belief that a womb was hanging out in someone's brain.

77 The Vagina Museum did a podcast on yoni steaming, and I'd highly recommend listening to it because our producers Hannah Hethmon and Alyssa Chafee did a deep dive and uncovered some very surprising stories.

All of these lies about the history of vaginal health treatments are there to provide a cover story for a company's true intentions – money-making. This is why knowing your stuff is so important.

The 'feminine hygiene' industry

If you're ever wondering whether a particular feminine hygiene product is necessary, here is the most important thing to know: **the vagina is self-cleaning**. And the vulva doesn't need more than an unscented cleanser.

These products tend to suggest that your normal vagina smells are bad, but many of these products don't help with hygiene – they can actually make it worse. Many have fragrances in them that are irritants or are the wrong pH (which can cause infections). If somebody is trying to sell you a soap to clean your vagina, they are either ignorant of how vaginas work or just want your money. There's only one kind of vulva soap I'll accept and that's soaps in the shape of vulvas. That's cute. But everything else in the entire feminine hygiene industry can go in the bin.[78]

Let's explore some of the products on the market and which, if any, are actually essential:

78 I'm obviously not including menstrual products here. But they shouldn't even be called 'hygiene' products. Menstrual blood isn't dirty.

Douches

Douching is the name for washing the inside of the vagina with a stream of cleaning liquid. It has been around for a very long time, but it really got going in the 1800s. In 1829, the medical journal *The Lancet* recommended douching 'six or eight times in the course of the day' to keep it squeaky clean! Douches were also often advocated as a form of contraception to remove sperm from the vagina. But once sperm gets past the cervix, no amount of douching can remove it – it's just too late. Even the disinfectant brand Lysol started marketing its product as a douche in the early 20th century and implied it could be used to kill sperm. These ads were pretty horrible, saying that your husband would hate you if you had a smelly vagina.

But douches don't clean your vagina – they can actually harm it. They cause microtrauma in your vagina by damaging the top layer of cells, disrupting the good bacteria living there and messing with the balance of the pH. They can actually end up making your vagina smell MORE by encouraging bad bacteria to grow there. Great news for the company though – you'll have to keep buying their product to combat that bad smell!

If your vagina smells off, that's usually due to an infection, and unless there are antibiotics in that douche, it isn't going to do anything. And that's the case regardless of whether the douche was made by some big company with lots of synthetic chemicals or by a small online seller with only 'natural' ingredients.

When someone has had a vaginoplasty to create a vagina, this is the only occasion where douching might be required, as these vaginas aren't self-cleaning. A doctor or surgeon can advise more on this.

Wipes

Another totally unnecessary product, I'm afraid. These products like to claim that they are for 'keeping you fresh after a workout', but honestly? Why are we giving our vulvas special treatment? I don't want athlete's foot, but when I searched for 'foot wipes' online, all that came up were general body wipes.

There are a few instances when you might want to consider using wipes for your vulva, such as if you are incontinent and need to keep extra clean to avoid skin irritation or if don't have access to cleaning facilities. In which case, you don't need specialized vulva wipes – just look for wipes with a pH as close to 5.5 as possible; don't get anything with a scent or fragrance and look at the ingredients list to avoid the following chemicals (which are irritants): formaldehyde, lanolin, tea tree oil, methylisothiazolinone and methylchloroisothiazolinone.

Vulva moisturizers

Yes, sometimes vulvas do get dry. It can be from pubic hair removal, chemotherapy, age, incontinence or even the type of products you use in the bath. If you know what's causing the problem, sometimes it's better to stop doing whatever is making your vulva dry (such as swapping out scented soaps for unscented cleansers), and sometimes it's better to moisturize. Look, you totally can moisturize if you want to – even if you don't have dry skin – but you don't necessarily have to. And here's the thing: you don't need a special vulva moisturizer or specialist product! Coconut oil, olive oil, baby oil or petroleum jelly will do just fine. Apply it to the labia majora, perineum and/or anus, but stay away from the labia minora and vestibule as they should be keeping themselves moist. Wait a few hours after applying oil-based moisturizers before having sex with latex condoms as oil can damage them.[79]

79 If you are moisturizing but your vulva is still dry after a few weeks, go and see your doctor to rule out any health conditions.

Vaginal deodorants

If you're not sick of my saying it by now, VAGINAS SMELL LIKE VAGINAS. Please, capitalism, you've got to stop. I'm getting tired. If your vagina smells off, go to a doctor. Changes in smells usually mean infections and you need treatment, not perfume.

Virginity restoring products

If this is the first you're hearing about this, I'm sorry we live in such a world. A virginity restoring product is something that claims to make your vagina tighter, so it 'feels' like you're a virgin again. Remember what we've learnt about virginity though – it is a social construct and if someone who's never had penetrative sex before feels 'tight', it's usually because they aren't aroused enough. These products usually work by irritating or drying out your vagina, which doesn't sound like a pleasant sexual experience. So you have to ask yourself, why are you doing it? It's usually for penile pleasure – but sex should be pleasurable for everyone. Any product that focuses solely on the pleasure of one person by making the experience unpleasant for the other is not a product worth buying.

Skin lighteners

STAY AWAY. Skin lighteners often contain very dangerous ingredients because OBVS – they are bleaching your skin. Vulva pigmentation is normal, and your body is beautiful just the way it is. If I could get you to do anything, it would be to spend more time on learning to accept your body than putting dangerous chemicals on it.

Your vulva is beautiful just the way it is.

What's that stain in my knickers?

Vaginal discharge is a completely normal and – in fact – vital process. Discharge is made of a combination of dead cells shed from the vaginal walls, secretions from the cervix and vestibular glands, and secretions from bacteria that live in the vagina. These secretions are how your body keeps the vagina clean!

Discharge SHOULD be clear or white, slippery and wet, and have a faint smell.

Discharge SHOULD NOT be green or dark yellow, very smelly or fishy smelling,[80] frothy, painful, itchy,

80 Yeah, vaginas are NOT supposed to smell like fish. How this came to be a standard belief and used to show how vaginas are dirty and gross will annoy me forever.

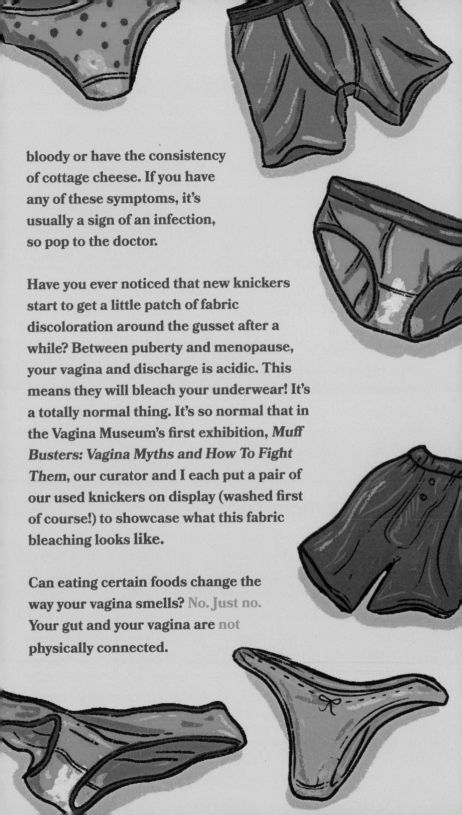

bloody or have the consistency of cottage cheese. If you have any of these symptoms, it's usually a sign of an infection, so pop to the doctor.

Have you ever noticed that new knickers start to get a little patch of fabric discoloration around the gusset after a while? Between puberty and menopause, your vagina and discharge is acidic. This means they will bleach your underwear! It's a totally normal thing. It's so normal that in the Vagina Museum's first exhibition, *Muff Busters: Vagina Myths and How To Fight Them*, our curator and I each put a pair of our used knickers on display (washed first of course!) to showcase what this fabric bleaching looks like.

Can eating certain foods change the way your vagina smells? No. Just no. Your gut and your vagina are not physically connected.

How *should* I keep my vagina and vulva clean then??

First, a quick refresher: the vagina is the tube that goes from the outside world to your cervix and the vulva is the external parts. When talking about cleanliness, it's really important to use the correct anatomical words because cleaning the vulva is one thing, and cleaning the vagina is a completely different thing.

Cleaning the vagina (i.e. DON'T)

The vagina does not need cleaning. That's because the vagina is SELF-CLEANING. That's just how magical it is. You literally don't need to even put water in it. It does the cleaning for you and removes anything it doesn't want via discharge. That's why my favourite part of the body is the vagina – it lets me be lazy as I want.

Cleaning the vulva

The labia minora and vestibule don't have sweat glands so they don't need routine cleaning, but you may want to use water to clean away anything, such as period blood, lube or ejaculate.

The rest of the vulva you can clean, but it's generally best to use an unscented, unperfumed cleanser as the skin is delicate. Don't use soap.

Quick chemistry sidebar: soap is actually a very specific type of chemical: a salt of a fatty acid.[81] It's a chemical we've been using for at least 5,000 years because it's so good at

81 This might be the only time in the whole book I get to use my chemistry A-level.

getting oils out of things. While that's great for the rather embarrassingly large number of times I've dropped chips on my jeans, oil is really important for skin health and using soap on the vulva will dry it out and disrupt its pH. In general, you'll want to use a soap-free cleanser on your skin. Yes, all your skin because it needs these oils. Have a look at the ingredients list. The most common soap is called 'sodium stearate'. You can use soap on your hands though. It's always boggled me that vulvas are considered dirty whereas hands aren't. Hands are actually super gross because we're always touching things with them.

A quick note on smegma

Smegma is the accumulation of dead skin cells and oils that collect around the genitals – penises and vulvas. It's white or yellow and often described as cheese-like (yes, I did just gag writing that). It isn't good to let it build up as it can get stuck in the folds of your labia and clitoral hood and cause discomfort. But don't worry, regular showers or baths should take care of it for you.

ALWAYS wipe front to back after going to the toilet. This helps stop the bacteria near your anus from getting near your urethral opening and helps prevent urinary tract infections (UTIs).

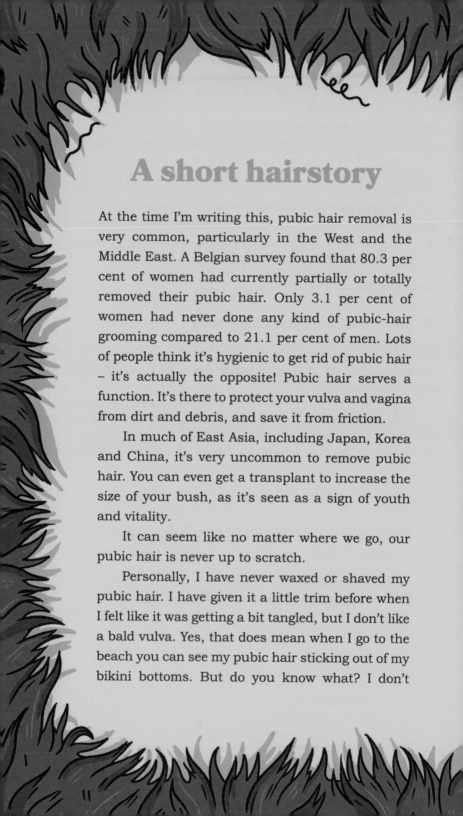

A short hairstory

At the time I'm writing this, pubic hair removal is very common, particularly in the West and the Middle East. A Belgian survey found that 80.3 per cent of women had currently partially or totally removed their pubic hair. Only 3.1 per cent of women had never done any kind of pubic-hair grooming compared to 21.1 per cent of men. Lots of people think it's hygienic to get rid of pubic hair – it's actually the opposite! Pubic hair serves a function. It's there to protect your vulva and vagina from dirt and debris, and save it from friction.

In much of East Asia, including Japan, Korea and China, it's very uncommon to remove pubic hair. You can even get a transplant to increase the size of your bush, as it's seen as a sign of youth and vitality.

It can seem like no matter where we go, our pubic hair is never up to scratch.

Personally, I have never waxed or shaved my pubic hair. I have given it a little trim before when I felt like it was getting a bit tangled, but I don't like a bald vulva. Yes, that does mean when I go to the beach you can see my pubic hair sticking out of my bikini bottoms. But do you know what? I don't

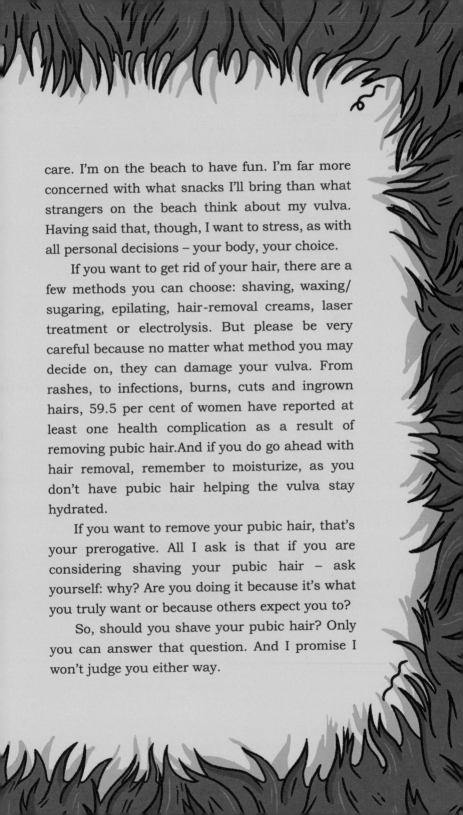

care. I'm on the beach to have fun. I'm far more concerned with what snacks I'll bring than what strangers on the beach think about my vulva. Having said that, though, I want to stress, as with all personal decisions – your body, your choice.

If you want to get rid of your hair, there are a few methods you can choose: shaving, waxing/sugaring, epilating, hair-removal creams, laser treatment or electrolysis. But please be very careful because no matter what method you may decide on, they can damage your vulva. From rashes, to infections, burns, cuts and ingrown hairs, 59.5 per cent of women have reported at least one health complication as a result of removing pubic hair. And if you do go ahead with hair removal, remember to moisturize, as you don't have pubic hair helping the vulva stay hydrated.

If you want to remove your pubic hair, that's your prerogative. All I ask is that if you are considering shaving your pubic hair – ask yourself: why? Are you doing it because it's what you truly want or because others expect you to?

So, should you shave your pubic hair? Only you can answer that question. And I promise I won't judge you either way.

The rise of labiaplasty

No two vulvas look the same – it's simply a fact of life. There is no 'right way' for your vulva to look. And yet for £4,000, there are surgeons who will cut off your labia, claiming to:

- 'Restore femininity'
- Stop it looking 'unappealing'
- Prevent 'poor hygiene'

Those are **real quotes** lifted from private surgeons' websites. **It's all lies**. They are saying these things so you'll buy their services.

A cosmetic labiaplasty is a surgery that reduces or reshapes the labia for purely aesthetic reasons.[82] It's one of the fastest-growing cosmetic surgeries round the world and according to the American Society of Aesthetic Plastic Surgery, requests for it in the US increased by 217.2 per cent between 2012 and 2017. In 2018, US women spent $35.7 million on labiaplasties alone. In the UK, the number of labiaplasties performed by the NHS has increased fivefold over ten years, and we have absolutely no idea how many have been done in the private sector.

Your labia minora are so important. They are involved in sexual pleasure because they contain lots of nerves and are connected to the clitoris. Why would you want to remove something that brings you pleasure?

There are also lots of possible complications of the surgery. You can experience pain, scarring and a decrease in sexual sensation and satisfaction.

---

82 You can also get labiaplasties for medical reasons, such as for removing cancerous tissue, repairing FGM or repairing tears in the labia, and of course that is a completely different issue.

It's also totally normal for labia to be large or asymmetrical. Mine are – I even measured them especially for you! My right one is literally double the width of my left. Your labia are more like **siblings**, not twins.

Why do people want small labia? It could be because the vulvas shown in mainstream porn tend to be smaller and not very diverse. Or perhaps it's due to the increased Western trend of shaving pubic hair, which makes labia more visible. Some people have even suggested it's because yoga pants have become so trendy, and they tend to show the outline of the vulva quite clearly. But no good-quality study has been done on this topic.

Society often feeds us the (false) idea that large labia are ugly, unclean and abnormal. This idea can be traced back to scientific racism in the 18th century, where colonialist scientists made sweeping false generalizations about the differences between the labia of Black and white women, with hugely harmful impacts. They said that Black women were more sexually promiscuous and 'deviant' than white women and argued that white women were less so due to their smaller, and therefore 'better', labia. It's absolutely disgusting, but that's really what many white supremacists thought – and this myth persists even today.

Many people say that their main motivation to get labiaplasty was to make their labia look 'normal'. But what even is 'normal'? It's time to throw the definition of the word 'normal' out the window and realize that all labia are unique. I encourage you to look at websites of The Great Wall of Vagina, The Vulva Gallery, the Gynodiversity project and The Labia Library and take in all the beautiful and diverse labia out there. Every single labium is normal and beautiful, including yours.

Pure, clean and natural

After reading about all the terrible things capitalism wants us to do to our bodies, I don't blame you if you need a break. We all need self-care. But is it really all about face oils, bath bombs and mindfulness apps with a £13-a-month subscription fee? No. It's about looking after yourself, truly and deeply. So light up a candle and take a bath if that's what works for you, but just know that you're not feeling better because of the bath bomb – it's because you chose to put your needs first. That's the self-care part.[83]

However you decide to do it, self-care is necessary or the world may end up tearing you down. Radical self-care is a concept that is thousands of years old, but I think Audre Lorde captured it beautifully in her 1988 essay 'A Burst Of Light':

> **Caring for myself is not self-indulgence, it is self-preservation, and that is an act of political warfare.**

Looking after yourself is one of the greatest ways to take a stand. It's more powerful than you might realize.

Red flags in the wellness industry

Here are some of the key words and phrases to look out for in wellness products. These are red flags because they either don't make sense, are misleading or just mean absolutely nothing at all:

---

83 I often think the reason we need the self-care in the first place is because of systemic oppression and the harms of capitalism. It almost feels like capitalism is trying to distract us by telling us we can buy ourselves into wellness, rather than taking responsibility itself . . .

Chemical-free

A chemical is anything made up of atoms. Everything you eat is chemicals. You are chemicals. The only things that aren't chemicals are things such as light and energy.

Rejuvenation

This doesn't mean anything medically. Technically it means to 'reverse ageing' but as of yet, no doctor can go back in time.[84]

Renewal

What does this even mean? Did my vagina come with a warranty???

Detox

'Detoxing' or 'cleansing' – removing toxins from your body – is something your liver and kidneys already do for you. Ask yourself: what specific toxins are they removing that your fabulous body doesn't already take care of?

Toxin-free

Whenever any company uses the word 'toxin', they are taking advantage of the fact that most people don't ask what toxin might otherwise be in it. The vagueness of talking about 'toxins' is a distraction. If they were truthful, they'd specifically say what toxins have been taken out.

Natural

Just because something is natural doesn't necessarily mean it's good. Lots of wonderful things *aren't* natural, such as glasses and sex toys, and lots of dangerous things are natural, such as poisonous snakes and lightning.

---

84 Except Doctor Who, of course.

Anything that gives impossibly fast results

They get those results by achieving the goal you want in a harmful way. Diet teas, for example, make you lose weight because they are laxatives. You poo the weight off – it's extremely harmful and you end up putting the weight back on almost immediately.

Superfood

This is a marketing term. Actual nutritional scientists don't use this word because it doesn't mean anything.

Boost your immune system

No one specific product can boost your immune system (except vaccines, of course).

Self-care for reals

- Booking a doctor's appointment if you need one
- Spending time in nature
- Resting without needing a reason
- Prioritizing good-quality sleep
- Taking time off when you're sick
- Doing a hobby you enjoy
- Telling people no when you can't help
- Asking for help
- Educating yourself
- Setting and enforcing boundaries
- Connecting with your community and the people you love
- Disconnecting from the hustle
- Standing up for yourself
- Moving your body. It could be exercise, dancing, dog walking – anything, as long as you enjoy it
- Expressing gratitude and love

- Turning off notifications
- Self-reflection, self-compassion and kindness
- Trusting yourself
- Leaving toxic relationships
- Crying
- Enjoying your food

Sometimes, it's not possible to practise self-care. It could be because day-to-day things are getting in the way, such as school pressure, friendship problems or responsibilities. Or it could be because of larger issues, such as exploitation or health problems. But my life changed when someone told me 'if something is worth doing, it's worth doing badly'. If you're feeling really low and like you can't even brush your teeth, just rinse your mouth with water. Something is always better than nothing, and we can only work within our capabilities.

We are enough

Capitalism has really done a number on us. It can make us feel like we're not good enough, and that we need to do or buy certain things to be worthy.

I want you to listen to me very carefully: **You are already enough.**

You may not feel that way, and that's OK. It sometimes feels like no matter what we do we'll never be acceptable for society. Never thin enough or curvy enough. Too confident or too meek. Too slutty or too frigid. So what's the point in criticizing yourself? Accepting that you'll never please society is liberating.

Learning that your worth is not tied to your appearance or any other thing that society tells you is important and takes work, energy and time.

I know it's easier said than done and sometimes we all feel bad about ourselves. But don't beat yourself up about it. We must instead practise self-compassion and be kind to ourselves in those moments. After all, you're the only person you are guaranteed to spend the rest of your life with. Don't you want to be a friend to yourself? If your friend came to you and said 'I'm a shitty person, I hate myself', how would you react? You'd probably comfort them, show kindness, help them move through those emotions and celebrate when they're on the other side. And they would do the same for you! And there's the trick – **you** can do the same **for you**. Imagine you are your own friend and treat **yourself** with kindness.

I want you to look at yourself in a mirror. Write down three things you like about yourself. You will get negative thoughts. Acknowledge them and allow them to move on. You're making a list of things you like – focus on that. Do it again the next day, but up it to four things. Then five things. What you're doing is practising being aware of the good and ignoring the negative thoughts. After time, hopefully those positive thoughts will come more naturally than the negative ones. You don't have to love your body, but you should respect it.

And remember that it's also OK to do what you need to survive. If you do something you don't really want to do – such as shaving your legs – it's not your fault. There is nothing to be ashamed of – and it's why I said I would never judge you for it. It's hard breaking away from what society has always told you is the acceptable way to be.

There are so many things you can do to make the world a better place for yourself. Follow people online who are positive about the things you might be insecure about. For example, if you don't like your big belly, follow people who have a big belly and love it. Stop consuming media that makes you feel bad and find media that makes you feel good about yourself. If you spot yourself comparing yourself to people on reality TV in a way that gets you down, try watching a different genre, listening to a podcast or picking up this book to remind you that you are PERFECT just as you are. Recognize that celebs spend enormous amounts of money, time and effort to look the way they do. Compliment your friends to foster a culture of kindness. Mix up compliments about appearance with ones about personality, interests and work. Stop using beauty filters, or be honest when you do. Call people out when they say Vs are smelly or disgusting. Show respect for the V and recognize that all of them are wonderful and normal.

I don't know if you can feel it, but I'm giving you a big hug. Together we can be revolutionaries. We can be anti-capitalists. We can practise self-care. We can be kind. We can find our big V energy. And we can realize that we and our Vs are already enough. I'm going to end this chapter with a few words from writer and poet Hollie McNish.

self-cleaning
cleaning your vagina
is like cleaning your throat
– you don't

intimate wipes
i don't want my vulva smelling
of lemon-scented washing lines
blossom will not turn to fruit
if soil is sick with pesticides

i am done with feeling dirty
just because my skin's alive
sometimes wet, sometimes sweaty
juice from the inside

my skin is not a show home
it's a home in which i play
i've no need of your products
or your shame

Chapter 10
THE FINAL CURTAINS

What can I do to make the world better for the V?

I truly hope that since you've got this far in the book, you are starting to love and adore Vs as much as I do. Welcome to the V-love club!

But I don't want to be dishonest with you – the world can be a difficult place for the marvellous V. Then again, you probably already knew that. And if we want to live in a world where all Vs are treated with the love and respect they deserve, we need society to change. You might think that sounds like an impossible, overwhelming task, but there is good news.

Society is a complex thing. It's a large group of people made up of millions – or even billions – of people at a time, all having thousands of tiny interactions a day. These interactions then form a pattern that when put together can be called a 'culture'. Although changing society takes time, with constant work and the help of lots of people, it's not impossible.

And it's also important to remember that humanity comprises many different cultures, and no one person's experience is the same. Depending on where you are born, your race, gender, sexuality, age and much more means that everyone has different battles to fight. So, it's going to take lots of slightly smaller fights, all of which are made up of little battles and skirmishes, to make big change. Even within our ranks, there will be disagreement on the best way forward. It's going to be messy and complicated, and it's definitely not going to be pretty.

But if we do want to change the world, it has to start somewhere. And it starts with you and me.

What sort of feminist are you?

If you're reading a book about the V, you're probably already a feminist. Throughout this book, there's feminism *galore*. And I think it's finally time to get to grips with it before you are released back in the world with your new-found V love.

There have been many forms of feminism, ever since women stood up and said enough is enough. The feminism that I shape my values by is called 'radical intersectional feminism'. This is a combination of:

radical feminism: the belief that we must totally dismantle oppressive systems and rebuild society in an equitable way, rather than simply making adjustments to our existing society.[85]

intersectionality: the understanding that all people exist at the intersection of multiple forms of oppression, which creates a unique experience for each person.

85 Feminism via adjustment is called reformist feminism.

Usually, the feminism we observe on television, social media and even from the mouths of our politicians is 'mainstream neoliberal feminism'. And although it has feminism in the name, it's not something that will actually help resolve the issues we want to face up to.

Mainstream neoliberal feminism is:

'lean in' feminism
(be a powerful woman by acting like a man)

'#girlboss' feminism
(the only thing that matters is individual action)

'this is what a feminist looks like' T-shirt feminism
(but the T-shirts are made in a sweatshop)

Some people called it 'pseudofeminism' because it looks like feminism, but when you dig down, it's not really. As Cinzia Arruzza, Tithi Bhattacharya and Nancy Fraser put it in their book *Feminism for the 99%*, this type of feminism is 'equal opportunity domination'. It's a system in which it's considered a step forward that it's a woman rather than a man busting a union, leading a war or doing other things that hurt women and marginalized genders.

It's a type of reformist feminism – the belief we shouldn't remove the existing hierarchy, just put some women at the top of it. It does this by focusing on individual advancement rather than societal advancement and means women can climb to the top and leave other marginalized people behind. This is why such 'feminists' are usually white, wealthy and cis – getting to the top of the hierarchy is a smaller jump for them than for other people.

Radical feminism, on the other hand, isn't just about changing certain laws that currently exist – it's about changing **all of society**. For example, strengthening laws around sexual assault won't help much if we don't address rape culture and prevent the problem from happening in the first place. The act of changing laws can only happen effectively if we also address the racism and sexism embedded in the system. Radical intersectional feminism is the only real way to achieve a fair and equitable world.

What do we do next?

The world isn't going to become a better place on its own. If it were, it would have done it already. The world becomes a better place because individual people start doing good things, which becomes groups of people and finally a whole movement fighting for what's right.

Now, I don't mean you individually have to change the whole world overnight. But what I do mean is that for change to happen, each person needs to play their part – from the schoolkid to the boss. And let's be honest, is that boss going to do what's right of their own volition? Probably not! But they will if you don't give them a choice – and you can do this by building power, applying pressure and staying true to your values. All of the examples on the following pages are revolutionary acts you can do for the V. There are so many fights to be had, and it would be impossible for one person to tackle them all. But you may find yourself drawn to just one for any number of reasons. You can use any of these activist strategies to support these struggles, and I have also included some specific actions you can take.

GOVERNMENTAL LEVEL

- Attend protests and marches for causes you believe in.
- Vote at local and general elections (once you're old enough!).
- Sign petitions for causes you believe in.
- Pressure your legislators to change the law by writing emails or phoning them.

INSTITUTIONAL LEVEL

- Boycott harmful companies.
- Support workers' strikes.
- Do a sit-in.
- Do a walkout.
- Create a manifesto of your values and principles.

COMMUNITY LEVEL

- Start or support existing campaigns and advocacy groups.
- Call out and call in when people are causing harm.
- Fundraise.
- Leaflet for important causes.
- Make connections with your community and practise mutual aid.
- Make speeches in support of issues you care about.
- Listen to marginalized people.
- Consciousness raising.

INDIVIDUAL LEVEL

- Educate yourself.
- Practise self-care.
- Donate money, if you can.
- Donate your time, if you can.
- Make more ethical consumer choices.
- Create art.
- Lead by example.
- Wear the symbol of your cause.
- Identify and confront your own biases and prejudices.
- Admit when you're wrong.

Reproductive justice

'Reproductive justice' is a term coined by the group Women of African Descent for Reproductive Justice. It refers to 'the human right to maintain personal bodily autonomy, have children, not have children and parent the children we have in safe and sustainable communities'. You can help in various ways.

- Fight **period poverty** by doing things such as getting your school/workplace/public spaces to provide free menstrual products in all bathrooms (yes, even the men's!), if they don't already.

- Advocate for **free and accessible contraception** by supporting universal free healthcare and talking to your friends about the different contraception options available.

- Join the struggle for **free, safe and accessible abortion** for example, by volunteering as an abortion clinic escort or supporting the people you love if they get an abortion.

- Advocate for **better OBGYN and sexual health care** by doing things such as raising awareness that healthcare needs to be inclusive for trans men and non-binary people with vulvas.

- Confront medical professionals who don't listen to you.

Sex and relationships

We all want to live in a world where our lives are filled with love and acceptance. You can help to do this.

- Promote **quality sex and relationships education** by asking your school to include important topics such as LGBTQ+ issues, sexual pleasure, health information, contraception options, bodily autonomy and information about healthy relationships and consent.

- Further our rights to **sexual pleasure** – for instance, by talking openly about sex and fostering shame-free spaces.

LGBTQ+ issues

For as long as humans have existed, there have been queer and gender non-conforming people. We all deserve to live without fear and as our true selves!

- Advance the **end of transphobia** by supporting people when they transition, actively making spaces trans-inclusive or raising money for shelters and charities that welcome trans people.
- Advocate for the **end of queerphobia** by attending Pride marches, and boycotting travelling to countries with anti-LGBTQ+ laws.

Culture

So many parts of patriarchal control are intertwined within culture, so dismantling it requires many arms to be addressed.

- Fight against **sexual assault and rape culture** – for example, by infusing enthusiastic consent into every area of your life and calling in victim-blaming and toxic masculinity.

- Take part in the effort to **end FGM** (female genital mutilation) – for instance, by raising awareness about this issue and educating yourself.

- Participate in **ending child marriage**, such as by advocating for girls' education. Or you could research and inform yourself about poverty elimination measures such as universal basic income.

Hafsa Qureshi (any pronouns)
Activist

Anyone can be an activist

In an ideal world, I wouldn't be an activist. I would live in a world where my identity as a brown, bi, genderqueer and disabled Muslim is nothing more than just a series of words. Where the cloth I wear on my head is just cloth. Where vulvas and vaginas are not assigned a gender, and pink and blue aren't either. But we're not in that world. Yet.

I fell into the world of activism purely by accident. My workplace LGBTQ+ network asked for more LGBTQ+ people of colour to take part, so I did. I didn't know my identity and being visible could be helpful to others. When I started to get involved in LGBTQ+ inclusion work, I received so many messages from people exactly like me, coming out to me and sharing their own experiences. All I did was make myself visible, inadvertently showing other people that they had the right to be seen too.

Now, I'm determined to fight for the rights that I know we deserve. Rights are not won through peace. When the large boot of fascism tries to step on us and our right to exist, we must not remain silent. We have power in numbers, and power in our voices. Our numbers make us harder to ignore. And having so many voices means we can fight harder against those in power, because we're much more difficult to suppress as a collective. If the way the world is bothers you, even just a little, consider joining the fight. The camaraderie and love you will find amongst other activists is like no other. There are thousands of activists across the world who may never march next to you but will always be by your side.

Activists can be loud, but we don't need to shout to be heard. Sometimes, we make change through quieter methods, like patience and paperwork, or across social media. These methods are no less important and are just as crucial to the work of everlasting change. If this side of activism appeals to you, look around at your school, workplace or local community groups. Use data to prove your point, that the hierarchical structures in place disadvantage marginalised groups. And if the data doesn't exist, perhaps now is the time to suggest that it should exist.

Anyone can be an activist. I've met people who believe they aren't 'good enough' or 'exceptional' and therefore believe they can't do it. But the truth is activism is for everyone. You don't need a degree to be an activist or 20 years in the field just to talk about your lived experience. Sometimes a bad thing happens, and everyone looks around. 'We all heard that teacher say something bi-phobic, why is no one doing anything?' We sometimes expect other people to step in first. Someone with more authority, or the power to change things. And that person never comes, because often they don't want to rock the boat. But you, dear friend, are going to rock that boat. Rock it until it falls over and we need to build a bridge. Then we can all cross those choppy waters in unison.

That's all activism is – being as annoying as possible!

A parting word

I LOVE my V. I hope, after reading this whole book, you love yours too.

Now you know all about the anatomy of the body, and as a result can take charge of your health and spread the knowledge. You know all about periods, reproduction and menopause, and how to be confident about the journey your V will take you on.

You know about sex and pleasure and how to love your V in the most literal sense. You know about being queer and all the different sexualities people around the world have.

You know how the V fits in to world culture, folklore and religion, and how vulvas have been celebrated and worshipped around the world. You also know how you can worship the V. You know about all the beautiful art of the V and can see its full beauty.

You know what all the parts are called, and why slang exists, and how to use language to demonstrate that there's nothing to be ashamed of when it comes to the V. You know how complicated sex and gender are, and how your V is just one part of it. You know about the effects of capitalism and how to truly look after your V in the face of it. You know about radical feminism and putting your V-love into practice and how to fight for the causes that matter to you.

Now you know the truth. No two Vs are the same. All are beautiful. All are complex. Vulvas are gods and goddesses. They are multifaceted. There are a thousand names for them. Vulvas are paintings and sculptures and music and rock art. They bleed. They don't bleed. They make life. They don't make life. Clitorises bring pleasure. Sometimes vaginas are wet, and sometimes they aren't. People with vulvas can love other people with vulvas. A person can have a vulva and be a woman, a man, non-binary, agender, two-spirit or gender fluid. Vs are magical and grounded and fantastical and real. The V is not one thing – it is *many*.

So many think the V is unknowable. But **now you know**. There's still so much more to learn, but I'm so happy we could start this journey towards loving, accepting, worshipping, prioritizing and embracing the V together. And there's always so much more to learn – you just have to look behind the curtain (pun definitely intended).

Acknowledgements

Unending thanks go out to so many people for making this book happen.

To all the people at Penguin, and especially to Phoebe and Sarah for editing. To Charlotte for believing in me before anyone else did. To Nadia for your amazing and beautiful creations.

To all the people who helped make the Vagina Museum happen, especially Kristina, Mae, Niharika, Sarah, Jenny, Jo, Stevie and Hana. To Zoe and Sarah, all the duty managers, volunteers, bar staff, techs and board advisers for being there, day in and day out, and without whom I would definitely have had a total breakdown.

To my amazing parents, for making me the confident, strong-willed woman I am today. To all my amazing friends who listened to me talk through ideas and filled up their WhatsApp messages – especially Katie, Tanith, Chloe, Ashlea, Fiona, Hannah and Tal. To Marc for all the endless cups of tea. To Scruffy for keeping my lap warm while I wrote. To Flora for all the puns.

To Miriam, the best person who ever lived.

To Sci-hub, Internet Archive and Z-Library, for uploading so many books and journals for free online and preventing me becoming bankrupt.

To all the activists, community organizers, campaigners, researchers, scientists, writers and artists working to make the world better for the V. I know we'll get there together.

Support groups, organizations and resources

The establishment have a history of messing things up, but I don't think there's a single person on the planet who doesn't have at least one thing they need help with. The beautiful thing about humans is that we are always seeking connections and understanding, and you'll quickly see that you are never alone. There are loads of support groups for people to share experiences and get support for a whole variety of medical conditions, trauma and advocacy. Here are a few of my faves. They are mostly UK-based as that's where I am, and so I can personally vouch for them. However, I'm sure ones more local to you are just a click away. Honestly, there are so many I couldn't possibly fit them all in this book – which I see as a great sign for hope! There are literally thousands upon thousands of people around the world fighting the good fight, and it is my honour and privilege to consider myself standing alongside them.

Gynaecological health

WEBSITES
Discharge Gallery, This Is A Vulva – thisisavulva.com/dischargegallery
The Eve Appeal – eveappeal.org.uk

BOOKS
My Broken Vagina – Fran Bushe
The Gynae Geek – Dr Anita Mitra
Our Bodies, Ourselves – Boston Women's Health Book Collective
Pussypedia – Zoe Mendelson and Maria Conejo
The Vagina Bible – Dr Jen Gunter
The Wonder Down Under – Dr Nina Brochmann and Dr Ellen Stokken Dahl

Vulva diversity

ARTWORKS
'The Great Wall of Vagina' – Jamie McCartney

WEBSITES
Gynodiversity – gynodiversity.com
The Labia Library – labialibrary.org.au
The Vulva Gallery – thevulvagallery.com

Periods

WEBSITES
AFRIpads Foundation – afripads.com
Binti International – bintiperiod.org
Bloody Good Period – bloodygoodperiod.com
Put A Cup In It – putacupinit.com
The Red Box Project – redboxproject.org
Tricky Period – facebook.com/TheTrickyPeriod

BOOKS
Period – Natalie Byrne
Red Moon Gang – Tara Costello

Sex and Gender

WEBSITES
Adventures In Time and Gender – adventuresintimeandgender.org
Gender Critical – ContraPoints (available on YouTube)

BOOKS
How to Understand Your Gender – Alex Iantaffi and Meg-John Barker

LGBTQ+

WEBSITES
galop – galop.org.uk
Gendered Intelligence – genderedintelligence.co.uk
The Outside Project – lgbtiqoutside.org
Stonewall – stonewall.org.uk

Switchboard – switchboard.lgbt
UK Black Pride – ukblackpride.org.uk

Intersex

InterACT – interactadvocates.org
Intersex Justice Project – intersexjusticeproject.org

Sex and relationships

WEBSITES
BISH – bishuk.com
Brook – brook.org.uk
CDC – cdc.gov/condomeffectiveness/Dental-dam-use.html
Scarleteen – scarleteen.com
Sexpression:UK – sexpression.org.uk
Sexwise – sexwise.org.uk

BOOKS
Come As You Are – Dr Emily Nagoski
Girl Sex 101 by Allison Moon
Sex Ed: For Adults – Ruby Rare
S.E.X – Heather Corinna

Reproductive Justice

WEBSITES
Abortion Rights – abortionrights.org.uk
Bedsider – bedsider.org
BPAS – bpas.org
Decolonising Contraception – decolonisingcontraception.com
Sister Supporter – sistersupporter.co.uk

Sexual violence

WEBSITES
Rape Crisis – rapecrisis.org.uk
Sisters Uncut – sistersuncut.org
The Survivors Trust – thesurvivorstrust.org

Sex work

WEBSITES

Decrim Now – decrimnow.org.uk

NUM – nationaluglymugs.org

SWARM – www.swarmcollective.org

BOOKS

Playing the Whore – Melissa Gira Grant

Revolting Prostitutes – Juno Mac and Molly Smith

Arts, culture and history

WEBSITES

The Feminist Library – feministlibrary.co.uk

Museum of Transology – museumoftransology.com

The Sheela-Na-Gig Project – sheelanagig.org

Queer Britain – queerbritain.org.uk

Vagina Museum – vaginamuseum.co.uk

Whores of Yore – thewhoresofyore.com

BOOKS

Fruit of Knowledge – Liv Strömquist

Sex: Lessons From History – Dr Fern Riddell

What Is Obscenity? – Rokudenashiko

News and journalism

WEBSITES

DIVA – divamag.co.uk

The Femedic – thefemedic.com

gal–dem – gal-dem.com

Radical feminism

BOOKS

Feminism, Interrupted – Lola Olufemi

Feminism Is For Everybody – bell hooks

Me, Not You – Alison Phipps

White Feminism – Koa Beck

Anti-capitalism

BOOKS

Feminism For The 99% – Cinzia Arruzza, Tithi Bhattacharya
    and Nancy Fraser

How To Be An Anti-Capitalist in the 21st Century – Erik Olin Wright

References

Chapter 1

Blackless, M., et al (2000). 'How sexually dimorphic are we? Review and synthesis.' *American Journal of Human Biology*, 12(2), pp.151–166.

UK Health Research Analysis 2014, Medical Research Council (www.ukcrc.org/wp-content/uploads/2015/08/UKCRCHealthResearchAnalysis2014-WEB.pdf)

PHE, 2018 (www.gov.uk/government/news/survey-reveals-women-experience-severe-reproductive-health-issues)

Chapter 2

ActionAid, 018 (www.actionaid.org.uk/latest-news/more-one-three-uk-women-face-period-stigma

Newsweek, 2016 (www.newsweek.com/nepali-girl-banished-menstruating-dies-makeshiftchhaupadi-shed-534725)

Endometriosis UK (www.endometriosis-uk.org/it-takes-average-75-years-get-diagnosis-endometriosis-it-shouldnt)

DeVito, Michael J., Schecter, Arnold. Jan 2002. 'Exposure assessment to dioxins from the use of tampons and diapers.' *Environmental Health Perspectives.* 110(1). 23–28.

www.tommys.org/pregnancy-information/im-pregnant/early-pregnancy/how-common-miscarriage

WHO, 2021 (www.who.int/news-room/fact-sheets/detail/abortion)

Rocca C. H., et al. (2015). 'Decision Rightness and Emotional Responses to Abortion in the United States: A Longitudinal Study'. *PLoS ONE* 10(7): e0128832.

Sajadi-Ernazarova K. R., Martinez C. L. (2022). 'Abortion Complications'. *StatPearls*.

Blue Cross Blue Shield, 2020 (www.bcbs.com/the-health-of-america/reports/trends-in-pregnancy-and-childbirthcomplications-in-the-us)

Birth Trauma Association (www.birthtraumaassociation.org.uk/for-parents/what-is-birth-trauma).

Chapter 7
The Eve Appeal (eveappeal.org.uk/blog/educating-eve/)

Chapter 9
Enzlin, P., et al (2019). '"To Shave or Not to Shave": Pubic Hair Removal and Its Association with Relational and Sexual Satisfaction in Women and Men.' *The Journal of Sexual Medicine*, 16(7), pp.954–962.

DeMaria, A. L., Flores, M., Hirth, J. M. and Berenson, A. B. (2014). 'Complications related to pubic hair removal.' *American Journal of Obstetrics and Gynecology*, 210(6), pp.528.e1–528.e5.

Briggs, L. (2000). 'The Race of Hysteria: "Overcivilization" and the "Savage" Woman in Late Nineteenth-Century Obstetrics and Gynecology.' *American Quarterly*, 52(2), pp.246–273.

Glossary

abortion: a medical or surgical procedure to end a pregnancy.

cervical screening: a medical test to assess the health of your cervix and look for signs of cancer and HPV.

cisnormative: when there is an assumption that people are cis.

colonialism: where one country controls another through direct means, such as by occupation and the military.

cultural appropriation: adopting customs or ideas from a marginalized culture in an inappropriate or offensive way.

erectile: tissue that fills with blood to get big and hard during sexual arousal.

fetishization: the process of making something desirable in a two-dimensional, reductive way, which is harmful.

gynaecology: the medical practice that deals with the V.

heteronormative: when there is an assumption that people are straight.

menopause: technically the day when you haven't had a period for one year. But it's more commonly used to refer to the few years when a person's body changes while their periods become less frequent, until they stop altogether.

misogyny: prejudice or hatred of women.

orgasm: a sudden involuntary release of sexual tension.

penetrative sex: when a penis or a sex toy goes into a vagina, mouth or anus.

social construct: something that exists only as a result of society and human interaction. This includes things such as money, borders, language and even morality.

two-spirit: a gender category that was formalized at the 1990 Third Annual Native American Gay and Lesbian Gathering. It's an umbrella term for the many genders within the 500+ Indigenous North American cultures.

Common health conditions everyone should know about

You might notice under a lot of these descriptions that 'no one knows what causes it'. That's because gynaecology research is massively underfunded compared to other medical disciplines due to institutional misogyny.

Ovaries

PCOS (polycystic ovary syndrome)

The three main symptoms of this condition are irregular periods, high levels of androgen hormones and cysts on the ovaries. Symptoms can include difficulty getting pregnant, excessive facial- and body-hair growth, weight gain and acne. No one knows what causes it. It affects about 10 per cent of people with ovaries.

Uterus

Fibroids

Fibroids are growths on the uterus. Only about one in three people with fibroids will experience any symptoms, which may include heavy or painful periods, pain during sex, constipation, lower back pain and abdominal pain. No one knows what causes them, but it probably has something to do with oestrogen. About one in three people with a uterus will get fibroids at least once in their life.

Endometriosis

This is a condition where the lining of the uterus grows somewhere that isn't the inside of the uterus. The main symptom is pain during periods, during sex and when going to the toilet. It can also cause heavy periods and difficulty getting pregnant. No one knows what causes it, even though it's extremely common and affects 10 per cent of people with a uterus between puberty and menopause.

Adenomyosis

This is similar to endometriosis, but the uterus lining grows inside the muscles of the uterus. Symptoms include heavy, painful and/or irregular periods and pelvic pain. It's totally unknown how many people with a uterus have adenomyosis, and estimates range anywhere from 9 to 61 per cent.

Urethra

UTI

UTI stands for urinary tract infection. Common symptoms are needing to pee often, a burning sensation when you pee, or having cloudy or bloody pee. It is said that the best thing to do to help prevent it is to pee after sex – the idea is that the whoosh of the pee will wash out any bad bacteria that's got in there. The data on the effectiveness of this technique is somewhat sketchy, but I guess it can't hurt!? What is proven to be important is to change condoms if you're changing where the penis/dildo is going in. Infections are super common, and will affect 50–60 per cent of people with a vulva at least once in their life.

Overactive bladder syndrome

This is when you very regularly get a sudden urgent need to pee. It affects 13 per cent of people with vulvas and for most, the cause is unknown. It can be treated with diet changes, bladder training, medication or, as a last resort, surgery.

Vagina

Thrush

Often people can experience thrush without it causing any symptoms or problems, but if you do have symptoms, they can include white, cottage-cheese-like discharge, itchiness and soreness while peeing and during sex. Some people are more likely to get it or to get it worse than others, and no one knows why. Roughly 75 per cent of people with a vagina will get it at least once in their life, and just over 6 per cent will get it recurrently.

Bacterial vaginosis

This is when the bad kind of bacteria start growing in the vagina as opposed to the good kind. The most common symptoms are a fishy smell and a change in discharge colour or consistency. It's really common and anywhere between 10 to over 50 per cent of people with a vagina will get it, depending on where they live in the world.

Vulva

Vulvodynia/vestibulodynia/clitorodynia

Vulvodynia is widespread pain of the vulva. If it's just the vestibule, it's called vestibulodynia; if it's just the clitoris, it's called clitorodynia. Vulvodynia can mean pain all the time, or only when the area is touched. No one is 100 per cent sure what causes it. It's not clear, but it could affect 10–28 per cent of people with a vulva.

Lichen sclerosus/lichen planus

Lichen sclerosus and lichen planus are auto-immune skin conditions of the vulva. Lichen sclerosus is of only the vulva, and lichen planus includes the vagina. These conditions somewhat increase the chances of getting vulval cancer. The main symptoms are itchy white patches on the skin. It's estimated it affects about 1.7 per cent of people with a vulva.

Pelvic floor

Incontinence

Incontinence is way more common than you might think! It can happen due to age, pregnancy, childbirth or other factors. It's very treatable and you don't have to put up with it nor is it just 'something to be expected and endured'. It's very much worth going to a pelvic-floor physiotherapist for treatment rather than endlessly buying packs of incontinence pads. It affects millions of people, and most people will get a form of it at least once in their life.

Pelvic floor muscle spasm/vaginismus

Pelvic floor muscle spasm (PFMS) is when the pelvic-floor muscles are always tight, and not relaxed. Vaginismus is when this happens only during or when anticipating vaginal penetration. It's quite painful and can be caused by a number of medical conditions or as a result of trauma. It's unknown how many people have this, as pain during sex for people with a vagina can be so normalized that many do not seek help.

Pelvic organ prolapse

This is when the pelvic organs like the uterus, bladder or bowel slip down from their usual position, often causing a bulge in the vagina. It's caused by the pelvic floor weakening, and can be due to childbirth, age, constipation or having to do lots of heavy lifting. Prolapse often responds very well to physiotherapy. It's estimated that 24 per cent of people with a vulva have some form of prolapse.

Multi-organ conditions

Cancer

There are five different gynaecological cancers – ovarian, uterine, cervical, vaginal and vulval. The symptoms are things we might be tempted to ignore, such as constantly feeling bloated, abdominal pain, itchiness in the vulva, or abnormal vaginal bleeding, e.g. after sex or between periods. You can learn more about these cancers by looking on the websites of gynaecological cancer charities such as The Eve Appeal, Jo's Cervical Cancer Trust and Ovarian Cancer Action.

FGM complications

There are roughly 200 million people around the world living with FGM. FGM, which stands for female genital mutilation, is a procedure to remove or sew up parts of the vulva. It causes a number of medical complications, such as pain, trauma, increased infections, complications in pregnancy and childbirth, pain during sex and mental health complications.

Index

Thank you to the following people who consulted on this book and provided their valuable expert opinions:

Katie Webb, specialist pelvic health physiotherapist

Gigi Engle, ACS, certified sex educator specializing in gender, sexuality and relationship diversity, and author of *All The F*cking Mistakes: A Guide to Sex, Love, and Life*

Neela Ghoshal, Senior Director of Law, Policy and Research at Outright International

Tammi J. Schneider, Danforth Chair of Religion at Claremont Graduate University

Isabelle Pan, co-founder, besea.n – Britain's East and South East Asian Network; secondary school teacher

Hans Lindahl, author and intersex media issues consultant

Justina Jang, consultant